Construction marketing

a professional approach

Paul Pearce

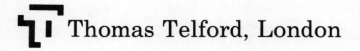 Thomas Telford, London

Published by Thomas Telford Services Ltd, Thomas Telford House, 1 Heron Quay, London E14 4JD

First published 1992
A CIP cataloguing record for this book is available from the British Library

ISBN: 0 7277 1652 2

Typeset in Great Britain by Alden Multimedia Ltd, Northampton, UK

Printed and bound in Great Britain by Redwood Press Limited, Melksham, Wilts

Contents

Introduction

'Customers for Brighton . . .' says the announcer at Victoria Station. That statement echoes music-hall associations which the town of Brighton may enjoy or may wish to live down. But it tells us that British Rail knows that its passengers are customers: not only do they travel, but they also pay. So it is with the construction industry. A client receives a service, but a customer pays for it. Professionals, contractors, subcontractors, suppliers and materials manufacturers alike, we are in business, and it is our customers who keep us there.

New ways of organising construction services have blurred the traditional boundaries between the professions and the contractors. Computer technology has provided powerful tools for design and management. Increasingly, design, construction planning and site work are interdependent and require new relationships between the designers, managers, builders and manufacturers. It is essential, therefore, for the benefit not only of individual firms but of the construction industry as a whole (and its customers) that it should address its market in a constructive manner.

All those in the categories mentioned above are 'professionals', and there is no room for an amateur approach to creating new business opportunities. Contractors can no longer rely on the professions to sell the industry's services to the outside world; consultancy firms can no longer rely on comfortable relationships to provide repeat order commissions year after year at scale fees, regardless of the quality of service. Creative thinking is required, about the needs of the market place and about how we can do things in new ways to satisfy those needs.

This book contains practical guidelines for a creative, professional approach to marketing in the modern competitive world. Its aim is to explain the concepts of marketing in terms of their application in the construction industry. To become an expert, you, the reader, will have to take a number of further steps. Undertake further reading on the subject of marketing (some recommendations are made), observe the commercial world around you, note how others shape up to seeking business at home and at work. Some lateral thinking is required in order to translate your observations into lessons for your own business situation. And the final step to really becoming an expert is to live, eat and sleep marketing, until in the manner of the eighteenth-century Viennese pastry cook who believed that all branches of the arts were mere departments of Viennese pastry cookery: you come to believe that all sectors of human endeavour are no more than applications of marketing.

There is no need for mystique about marketing: this book will have succeeded if a significant number of its readers believe that it contains nothing other than common sense. It aims to be a readable, practical and *useful* statement of the application of modern marketing techniques to the needs of the construction industry. It is offered at a time when the industry has begun to recognise the need for professional marketing; a time of limited order books, when minds are focused on getting work.

It used to be said that 'a good wine needs no bush'. We may be assured, however, that of two good wines, the one with the bush is the one that sells.

1 Marketing construction services

Formal marketing in the UK construction industry is a young art. For almost a century after the industrial revolution, the professionals led the industry's systematic external efforts to obtain work. Architects and engineers, bound by very English rules of conduct which owed as much to the social tradition of English Gentlemen as to the ethics of business, sought commissions from the patrons of the industry. Contractors, with less inhibition, wooed the professionals for a chance to tender for the opportunity to build their designs. Both groups worked hard to obtain work, but the professionals had almost to pretend that they were not in business and that, as gentlemen, they were merely responding to their peers' requests for service. The contractors depended so heavily on the goodwill of the professionals that they were reluctant to take any step that the professionals might see as a potential threat to their monopoly of the direct relationship with the client. This historical relationship is crystallised in our 'third party' contracts. Even today, quite substantial contracts may be entered into and the works executed without the two parties to the contract ever meeting.

For decades, this inflexible structure inhibited our industry's creative response to the needs of its clientele, and may well have limited its contribution to economic growth. Since the Second World War, two significant trends have progressively freed the industry from its inhibitions. The greater, of course, is the impact of modern technological, industrial and economic development on the way our businesses seek to control their own destinies. Professional management plans for success with a clear mind; real barriers and boundaries are distinguished from merely traditional ones. The other trend, perhaps less global but nevertheless of great significance, is the bringing up to date of the rules by which our 'Professionals' are guided.

Our Victorian grandfathers (or at least those that made the rules) saw two kinds of professionalism. There were professionals as distinct from amateurs, and Professionals as distinct from tradesmen. The rules for the non-amateur professionals contained the strong social element which, for example, in English cricket, separated the Gentlemen from the Players into the second half of the twentieth century. The rules for the professions

1

were designed to ensure that the client received the highest possible standards of service, delivered in a manner that protected his interests. But they had the incidental effect of sheltering the professions from all but the most gentlemanly of competitive forces. The social and economic environment in the closing decade of the twentieth century permits neither of these concepts to survive. In sport the emphasis is on fairness and on protecting the spectator from the worst forms of distracting commercialism. In business (and all of us are in business; Professionals, contractors and tradesmen), care must be taken to distinguish between rules that genuinely protect clients' interests and rules that act in restraint of trade.

What is marketing?

The 'market' is the economic mechanism that governs the relation of supply and demand. So 'market-ing' can be seen as the recognition and use of the economic and other forces that exist within the market to create business. Hence it is as an engine for the economy. Marketing identifies economic needs, creates the products to satisfy those needs, and by bringing the two together it fulfils its primary objective of creating business.

In down-to-earth industries such as construction, the very concept of marketing has been mistrusted. Hardbitten contractors (and perhaps consultants, who used to pretend that they were not hardbitten) thought of marketing as a superficial activity. New work was obtained by doing a good job and by moving in the circles in which clients would be met. This 'marketing' business, with its travelling salesman image, high-pressure selling and perhaps even a touch of misrepresentation, might dupe the housewife when she bought a can of baked beans or a vacuum cleaner, but it would not do for sophisticated clients.

It may be that marketing was just not understood, or that it was underestimated. How many times has one heard someone in a contracting organisation, when work is a bit slow coming in, say that Joe should be taken off site for a few months 'to do some marketing'. This means that Joe will call on some architects and ask for opportunities to submit tenders in competition. Marketing is rather more than that, as we shall see.

Marketing is the recognition and use of the economic and other forces that exist within the market to create business. The Chartered Institute of Marketing has adopted the following succinct definition:

> Marketing is the management process responsible for identifying, anticipating and satisfying customer requirements profitably.

At first sight, this statement may seem rather glib. The cynic may see it as a typical product of the slick and superficial marketing mind. This is not true: it will become clear as the principles of marketing are examined that these 14 words summarise them in a most remarkable way. Readers new to the discipline of marketing may wish to memorise this definition as a valuable reminder of what marketing is about.

Marketing is like all other areas of human endeavour. If we can achieve a clear understanding of the underlying principles, the rest is relatively easy. The next few pages, therefore, aim to explain those principles in terms familiar to those who know something of business in a construction environment. Undiluted market-speak will be avoided; specialist terms will be defined as necessary. The aim is to bring the reader to the point of take-off without straying too far from the familiar world, while referring, by way of illustration, to the kind of consumer marketing activity with which we are all familiar as individuals.

Some companies are described as 'market-led'; others are labelled 'product-led'. The former make what they know they can sell; the latter try to sell what they have in stock or what they happen to make. The difference between the two is central to our understanding of marketing.

Consider an imaginary medium-sized joinery company. Throughout its long business history it has developed an enviable reputation for short production runs of very high quality, architect-designed fitted furniture. During the banking boom of the 1980s, it expands considerably and devoted its whole production capacity to high quality, bespoke dealing-room furniture. The firm's 'setters out' are skilled advisers to architects and interior designers, capable of translating their design concepts into efficient, elegant fittings. By 1990, the banking and financial services industry has installed more dealer desks than it will be able to use again until after the turn of the century. The market for the company's newly specialised product collapses. A few modest dealing rooms are being created by new players in financial niche markets, but in the light of recent experience, their owners are furnishing them with caution.

What is to be done? The firm's perception is that it is a manufacturer of high quality bespoke dealing room furniture, in a highly profitable market. It has made a great deal of money from financial services clients who indulge every whim of their prima donna moneymakers on the trading floor. It has a high reputation for quality and for a positive flexible response to the last-minute changes and unusual requests endemic to the installation of dealing rooms. The company's clients are willing and able to pay for that level of service. There are fewer opportunities, but it is still the market leader; it has come to expect orders even when its price is not the lowest; it will survive where others fail. It decides to tighten its bidding prices a little, take on two more salesmen and push on.

But the market has changed. The clients are minimising capital investment in facilities and watching their overheads very carefully. The prima donna on the trading floor no longer pushes his luck for mere furniture. He has seen too many of his peers get the sack. New dealing rooms are equipped with relatively low-cost standard desks. The company tries to compete with them on price, but fails to achieve quality, value for money, profit, or any new business! A hundred years as cabinet-makers to the building trade is apparently at an end.

Alternatively, the company could sit back and take stock of its business. What business is it really in? It is a skilled joinery firm, equipped for high-quality work in medium-length production runs. The question to be asked, therefore, is 'In the current state of the economy, who is likely to want to buy, or be persuaded to buy, something that we could make economically and sell convincingly?'

At a semi-creative level of thinking, it considers what people and firms are buying at the present time. Are they buying dealing-room furniture? No! Kitchens? Not with mortgage rates as high as they are! Bar furniture? Perhaps—pubs are full in bad times and the breweries are going through changes. And so on. Then, of the things that are selling, which can the company make most easily with the least change in workforce and the least new investment, if any? Can it easily gain access to the customers to sell the product? If it decides on domestic kitchens, for example, will this entail a whole new approach to selling into the hitherto unknown retail market? It is geared to high-quality work. Is the chosen market willing to pay the price of quality? What could be said to convince them? Who is selling similar products?

Or, at a really creative level of thinking, the company considers the economic, social and demographic (a good 1990s buzz-word) conditions. What might nobody yet have thought of, in the general area of its capability, that would tap a rich vein of potential need? It is very good at medium runs of high-quality woodwork, but has little experience of consumer marketing. People nowadays have increased leisure—some of it enforced —and while they think carefully about major expenditure, there is a lot of capacity for day-to-day expenditure on aesthetically satisfying leisure activity. The order book is reasonable for six months, but beyond that something new is required.

Careful analysis of these strengths, weaknesses, opportunities and threats (the classic SWOT analysis) leads to the invention of a new game: a kind of indoor golf in which the obstacles and objectives are portable furniture-like constructions, and the clubs are large polished hardwood spoons. When not in use in a club-room, the whole set, carefully placed around the edges of the space, adds pleasingly to the decor. A prototype is made. It is different, slightly outrageous, and priced at £5000. Preliminary enquiries suggest that social clubs and leisure centres would be interested. It is shown on 'Tomorrow's World'. With little effort enough is sold to commit the company's existing manufacturing capacity for twelve months. It becomes a craze. A deal is done with a retailer to market a domestic version, and so on. This is a deliberately improbable idea, but the process of thinking is real. In the latter case, the company was market-led, considering first what the customer would buy and second whether and how it could make it.

This is not to suggest that every joinery firm in the nineties should convert its output to the manufacture of leisure hardware. Far from it. But the example illustrates the difference between the internalised, product-led approach and the broader, externalised, market-led approach.

Most of us become architects, engineers, quantity surveyors, construction managers or builders because we enjoy the work. In the office, we wrestle with the problems of design and create something that satisfies us; we seek publicity for our designs in the technical press to impress our professional peers. On site, the tough business of getting things built more or less right to time and cost, the necessary confrontation between the parties to contract and subcontract, and problems of labour, materials delivery and the weather are overriding concerns. Our minds are rightly focused on the day-to-day operations that earn us our living. But we must remember that these operations are not an end in themselves. We are doing them for the benefit of a client; that client is paying us to do them, and he and other clients will be the ones to decide whether or not their next job is our next job.

If our operation is efficient, everything we do is directed towards fulfilling our service obligations to the client. Every individual, therefore, may affect the client's perception of our performance and of the quality of the service we provide. Little comment is needed here about our main-line services. Either we provide efficient, economic designs which meet the client's needs, we build well and complete on time, we manufacture specialist components to meet requirements and deliver them to site on time, or we do not! Those are the minimum requirements of our business. But do we send the client well set-out letters, neatly folded in the envelope with the stamp put on straight? What happens when he telephones our office, site or works? What happens when he visits it? When we undertake to send a drawing or an invoice, is it done today, and is it right first time? Trivial matters, you may say. But think about it. These are the things each of us remembers about the organisations we deal with. These are the things which, regardless of main-line performance, determine whether we think well or badly of a firm. They affect what we say about it to our friends and colleagues, who may also be its future clients.

In a market-led business, from the chairman to the office junior, from the site agent to the tea lady, everyone is a salesman. Each person knows that his or her performance and behaviour is an important part of the quality of the organisation, and how that quality is perceived by the client.

5

Returning to the Chartered Institute of Marketing definition of marketing as 'the management process responsible for identifying, anticipating and satisfying customer requirements profitably', note that marketing is, first of all, a management process. Management must ensure that the whole organisation is dedicated to the service of its clients and the satisfaction of their requirements. Before we can satisfy any requirement we must identify it; but more important still, if we are to be one jump ahead of our competitors we must think ahead and anticipate requirements. What will be needed in a few years' time? What 'needs', indeed, can we create? When all is said and done, we must be profitable. Profit is what will make sure that we are still here serving our clients next year.

Every purchase, whether a can of baked beans or a jumbo construction contract, is the result of a specific decision to buy. If we are to join the ranks of the really successful, profitable, market-led companies, our whole business strategy, our corporate planning, our marketing strategy and our sales efforts must focus directly on that decision to buy. This is a very simple concept but, like keeping one's eye on the ball in cricket or tennis, it is one of the rules that simply and uncannily make the difference between winning and losing.

As we consider the steps in the developing relationship which lead the customer towards an eventual decision to buy, we shall return time and again to another simple but important underlying principle. Our whole marketing process is one of persuasion. It is always easier to persuade people to accept our point of view, or to do what we want, if we look at the matter from their point of view. To see their point of view, we must understand their objectives and what motivates them. At each stage in our thinking, we shall remind ourselves of the need to place oneself in the position of the customer, and to act in a manner that will tend to make him *want* to do what we want him to do.

Remember Aesop's tale of the sun and the wind having a competition to see who could make the traveller take his coat off. The wind's blowing and threatening only made the poor traveller button his coat more closely and resolve to protect himself. The sun knew that if the traveller felt warm and comfortable, and did not feel threatened, he would soon want to take his coat off.

Chapter 2 deals with marketing strategy: the process of deciding what business we are in, what products or services we should offer, to whom we should offer them, for what price and with what inducements to buy. In thinking about the strategic planning of our efforts to secure business we shall need to understand some of the basic principles of marketing. As far as possible, we shall look at them wholly in the context of our own industry. Understanding how they apply in a familiar business context will provide a background against which to tackle a wide range of more general marketing literature, some of which is recommended at the end of the book. The remaining chapters aim to be a practical guide to organising our marketing activity and improving our performance.

We are concerned with practical marketing, with getting work, with the application of principles to our business rather than with the principles for their own sake.

How can the principles that sell soapflakes be applied to the construction industry

As individual consumers and members of twentieth-century society, we are inundated with pressures to buy. Advertising in the press, on radio and television, on hoardings carefully placed where we stop at the traffic lights, and in every other possible medium of communication, offers to satisfy needs we may not even know we have. Most of our domestic mail seems to consist of unsolicited approaches from booksellers, financial institutions, mail-order firms, or someone else who is trying to sell us something—so-called 'junk mail'. Everything in the supermarket—the packaging, the layout of the store, the design of the fixtures, the soft music and seductive voices on the public address system, easy car parking, the helpful staff, the simplicity of paying with a plastic card—is there to make us fill our trolley.

Not only are we exposed to this pressure, but our press and television analyse the process daily. Without realising it, we become part of the marketing culture. Someone with a clipboard stops us in the street to ask us what toothpaste we use. Would we change to a new green-coloured product that tasted of figs? We are aware of market research. We buy shaving cream in a part of the country we are visiting and find that the product we have used, man and boy, is in a different pack and has a new fragrance. We experience product development. Our credit card company sends us a very glossy magazine which advertises incredibly expensive watches, cars, travel, collectors' pieces, and other things with messages designed to appeal to those who think they have 'arrived'. We notice that our local supermarket concentrates on own-label products, promoted on value for money; another branch of the same retailer offers exotic canned soups, expensive cheeses and fine wines. We are subject to market segmentation. We may not know or articulate these terms of art, but we are well aware of the concepts.

We know a great deal more about marketing than we realise, and most of what we know comes from our experience of the consumer goods market in which, like it or not, we are all very active participants. The initials 'FMCG' that we see in advertisements for salesmen stand for 'fast-moving consumer goods'. The FMCG sector is the core of the marketing world: not only is our cultural perception gained here, but most general marketing literature is based on consumer markets.

Are there principles common to the marketing of consumer goods and of construction services? We shall see that there are. First we decide what business we are in. What is it that our customers expect to gain when they buy from us? What is the 'product' the customer buys? The product is not always what it seems. We certainly do not pay £20–£30 for an eggcupful of alcohol and a few grams of soluble aromatic chemicals. We pay for the ideas that surround the wearing of perfume. A newspaper publisher is not in the business of printing and selling newspapers—the reader buys information or entertainment. Most contractors are not directly in the business of supplying buildings. Most customers, property investors apart, have no primary interest in the building, but in the shelter and other facilities it provides. The architect, as a contractor's customer, buys a service to realise his design. It is important that we understand what our customer buys. As the market changes, we must know how to change our response. The builder, subcontractor or component manufacturer, in shaping that part of his business which serves architects, must pay as much attention to the service he provides to the professional client as he does to the efficiency of production and to the quality of the end product.

As consumers, we buy one brand of toothpaste or canned drink rather than another similar product in response to information we receive from the manufacturer and the distributor. We believe the product will do something for us because the advertising has told us, or suggested, that it will. The information comes through advertising, through other means of mass communication, from displays at the point of sale or from the design of the product or its packaging. Our attention is drawn to the price and to that of competing products. We become predisposed to buy the product. We take a decision to buy it by placing it in our supermarket trolley. There have been a set of marketing decisions about the product and how it should be presented to us. The cost-effective way to communicate with 50 million users of toothpaste is by mass advertising and information at the point of sale. The communication is directed where the target customer will receive it. Recorded rock and pop music is advertised in tabloid newspapers and in specialist magazines read by young people; expensive waxed overcoats, Range Rovers and green wellies are advertised in 'county' magazines and in the colour supplements of the Sunday 'heavies'.

In most sectors of construction, potential customers can be numbered in thousands rather than millions. We therefore find other cost-effective ways of communicating with them. We must still identify what our product is. We must find out where our customers are, whether or not they want what we propose to offer, what their alternatives are, whether or not they will pay the price we can afford to sell it for (or more), what arguments will convince them, and how we can identify them and get our message to them.

It is a different version of exactly the same game.

Business-to-business marketing of services

We now return to the twin concepts of the 'decision to buy' and 'placing oneself in the position of the customer'. By far the greater part of the work of medium-sized and large firms in the construction industry is obtained from other 'business' customers in the public and private sectors. Our systematic efforts to obtain new work are, therefore, aimed at other businesses. Where and who are these businesses? How do they take decisions? And how do we read their minds?

In the next few chapters we shall see that there are relatively few companies in most target sectors, and we shall consider the numerous formal and informal sources of information about them. The important difference between the retail marketing of consumer goods and the business-to-business marketing of substantial parcels of service, which underlies all our thinking about marketing, can be expressed quite simply. In consumer marketing, the customer must know about our product. We know generically about the customer as a member of a group with certain needs and motivation. But we may never know him as an individual. In business-to-business marketing of custom-delivered services, it is more important to know the customer than to be known by him.

Retailing is like fishing with a net. We know what fish we want and when and where they swim and feed. We obtain a suitable net, pull it through the water where they are, catch large numbers and never know how many get away. There are plenty more at the fishing grounds tomorrow. If we fish at the wrong time, in the wrong place or with the wrong net, we do very badly.

Our kind of business-to-business marketing is more like hunting a bear. We know we are after bear, and we know bears' habits and habitat. We identify an individual and stalk it. Only when we move in for the closing transaction does it know who and where we are.

The business 'decision to buy' may be taken by an individual, but that individual decision-maker will be influenced by a complex structure of advisers and others. Access to each of these people will be gained through the good offices of telephonists, receptionists, assistants and secretaries. Placing ourselves in the position of the customer organisation, therefore, involves identifying all such contributors to the particular decision-making process that affects us, and understanding how their internal process works. This understanding must then be used to align our advantage with that of the decision-making complex.

Construction services marketing

In construction industry marketing, there is always some debate about the use of the word 'product' to describe what we sell to the customer. With the exception of a few sectors, our industry provides services. In marketing jargon, we think of the product as whatever it is that the customer buys. A load of 5000 bricks is undeniably a product; the team of bricklayers who put them in place provide a service. The firm that employs the bricklayers probably offers a range of services: bricklaying, plumbing, joinery etc. However, the 'product' that the main contractor customers buy may well be no more and no less than the procurement of skilled labour. It is therefore convenient to think of what the customer buys as a 'product'. We shall adopt this terminology.

The industry's business-getting process

The construction industry obtains business in relatively large pieces. The client's decision to proceed, and to do so with us, that is his decision to buy, will be taken in his own good time and in the light of his chosen criteria. We obtain business by being there, in the right relationship with the client, at the time the decision is to be taken.

Our initial marketing effort goes into deciding which customers to pursue. We then find out who the decision-makers are, and seek to build relationships with them. For such a relationship to be productive, the client must see real benefit from it. The need for relationship-building is almost universal. Even the contractor, subcontractor or supplier who does no more than seek opportunities to submit competitive tenders to architects and public sector authorities has first to gain the confidence of the client's formal or informal 'approved list' maker. He must then stay in touch with the individuals who decide the actual tender list. From that level upwards, the relationship-building process becomes more complex, and its aims more sophisticated. We shall deal with this whole process in chapter 5.

Corporate strategy

In dealing with marketing, reference must be made to corporate strategy. In a market-led business, corporate strategy and marketing strategy are inseparable. Marketing is not done solely by the marketing department. Just as war is too important to be left to the generals, marketing is too important to be left to the marketing people! It is a state of mind and of policy for the whole business. The aim of the business is to undertake profitable activity. The only source of that activity is our customers. And as we have seen, it is the marketing process that identifies those customers and anticipates their requirements.

To illustrate this point, we come back to the 'product-led'/'market-led' question. In an established business we may say to ourselves, 'Think of all these people who work for us. What new sources of work can we find for them?' Or when sales are flagging, we may ask where else we can sell our tried and tested product. A business based on these concepts is very likely to fail because it may well be relying on business that is no longer available. In considering the future, we must take the broadest definition of 'what business we are in' and examine what customers exist for the things we could offer. Having accepted that discipline, we can then consider how our people and our plant can respond to the new situation.

'Market-led' means *led by the market*. We must shape ourselves up to offer the goods or services we know customers will buy. These are not necessarily the goods we find it most convenient to make, or the services we most enjoy providing!

Marketing strategy

We shall deal in detail with marketing strategy in chapter 2. The purpose of the strategy is to identify the products (meaning both physical products and services) that we intend to offer, the kinds of customers to whom we shall offer them, the means by which to approach the customers and the arguments we shall use.

We must assemble information, analyse it and reach informed judgements with great care. But we must not let the preparation of the strategy become an end in itself. Data and analysis are only of value in the conclusions they provide. Overemphasis on the analytical process, or worse still, the idea that we can calculate the answers, will lead to difficulties. We must aim for entrepreneurial judgement based on what information can be made available. The alternative is known as 'analysis paralysis'!

The rationale as well as the conclusion of the strategy must be recorded. This will give a basis for coping with circumstances for which the strategy does not provide. Also, we must make sure that the strategy is our servant rather than a tyrant under which we have to serve until we reach the time ordained for its review. If market conditions change, we must bring forward our review. And we must remember that the marketing strategy is a plan for efficient, systematic efforts to get us the business we want. We must conduct our business in an orderly manner, but we must not close our eyes to unforeseen opportunities.

What is meant by 'positioning'?

'Positioning' is a word much used by marketing people, and sometimes misused by others. What does it mean? As we have seen, in thinking about marketing strategy we must choose, from the great number of products or services we could offer, those with which we are most likely to succeed. For each product or group of products, there is a range of options of quality, price, type of customer etc. To enable our customers to understand us, we must make it clear where we stand within these various ranges.

In the 1930s, F.W. Woolworth's chain store positioning was very clear. They called themselves 'Nickel and Dime Stores' or in the UK 'Threepenny and Sixpenny Stores'. They offered what quality they could for those prices. They relied on a high volume of sales from a mass market of people who could afford to spend small sums on all kinds of domestic and personal goods. At early 1990s' prices it would be, perhaps, a 50p and £1 store. That is a 'bargain basement' positioning. At the other end of the scale, Harrods was and remains positioned as the top people's store. Not quite 'If you have to ask the price, you can't afford to shop here', but tending to serve those who want the best and can afford it. Most of us will not have heard of the 'If you have to ask the price...' stores. They promote themselves within the exclusive market sectors for which they are positioned.

In the construction industry, positioning may be less visibly defined, but it is nevertheless there and necessary. Individual contractors are positioned by the quality and unit value of work they seek, the level of risk they are willing to take, etc. Consultants are more recognisably positioned by the size and quality of client and project they target, and by their willingness or otherwise to provide a tightly defined service for cut-price fees.

Responsibility for marketing

As we have seen, the marketing 'idea' must permeate the whole organisation. It must be a basic element of the culture. But line management responsibility for direct efforts to obtain work must coincide with responsibility for financial performance. No manager should be allowed to be in a position where he can say that he has kept overheads within budget, he has made the required margin on each individual contract, but his business has not made a profit because the marketing department has not provided him with the necessary turnover.

Keeping on track (the marketing audit)

How do we know how we are doing? Is our strategy clearly stated and understood? If it is, are we acting on it? Have the day-to-day needs of the business caused informal changes? If the business is performing, is it because of our marketing activity or in spite of it? Could we be doing better? Is there an opportunity or a problem around the corner? Chapter 11 suggests a technique for periodic auditing of our whole marketing activity to check that we are still on track, and to put us back on the rails if necessary.

2 Marketing strategy

The aim of marketing strategy and its relation to corporate strategy and business planning

Professional firms have traditionally obtained new work by being well known in the local community and among their professional peers. They did not, in general, make overt approaches to potential clients. Contractors were not restricted by formal codes of conduct. But they did rely on the goodwill of the professional firms that provided their bread and butter in the form of opportunities to compete for third-party contracts. They were therefore reluctant to bypass the professionals in seeking direct relationships with the construction industry's external clients. To the professionals, therefore, 'marketing' meant building relationships within client and professional circles, hoping to be invited by the client to take part in new work, or to gain introductions by referral through fellow professionals. To the contractors, it meant knocking on the professionals' doors.

This relationship-building, inside and outside the industry, remains the central theme of the modern business-to-business marketing of services of the kind offered by architects, consultants and most contractors and subcontractors.

So, what does 'marketing' offer beyond a few ideas for doing these traditional things more effectively? The key lies in a set of concepts and techniques we can call marketing strategy. But what is marketing strategy, what difference does it make, and how do we do it?

Without a marketing strategy we may sit at our desks, scratching our heads, wondering wherever all the new work we need is going to come from. With an effective marketing strategy, we have a clear plan which tells us where our best customers are, what we should be offering them, how we should approach them and what we should be saying to them to convince them to buy from us rather than our competitors. The better our strategy, the nearer we are to only having to walk around and pick up the orders! If we are market-led, the marketing strategy is the core of our corporate strategy and, as such, the basis for our business plan.

Strategy means planning future action. Like many other words that are now part of the vocabulary of business management, it has been adopted from military language. We say that an activity we admire has been planned and executed with the precision of a military operation; soldiers knew the value of planning centuries before business management was invented. An army plans its warlike campaign in the light of its own military objectives, the intelligence it can gain about the enemy, the terrain, the weather, its own strengths and limitations, its ability to supply itself on the move, and so on. It certainly does not line up its infantry, tanks and artillery wherever they happen to be, and make a frontal attack on the place where the enemy was last seen! The idea of doing so seems absurd. We know what happened to the Light Brigade 'theirs not to reason why'.

Marketing strategy asks the 'reason why'. Our 'Light Brigade' is the resources we are able to commit to seeking new business, and marketing strategy makes sure that its efforts are directed towards achieving our business objectives, in the manner most likely to succeed. Before we can plan the achievement of our business objectives, we must say what they are. And in examining how to achieve them, the objectives themselves must come under scrutiny. We may discover that it is easier to achieve slightly different business objectives from those we first thought of: we may even find that the latter cannot be achieved, and that we are obliged to adopt others.

Combining the Chartered Institute of Marketing definition of marketing given in chapter 1 and the definition of strategy given above, we can say that:

> Marketing strategy is the management process responsible for planning future action to identify, anticipate and satisfy customer requirements profitably.

Marketing strategy is therefore that part of the corporate strategy and business planning process which considers the needs of customers. It identifies those customers on whom we should concentrate, anticipates their needs and plans how we should set about satisfying them.

In more practical terms, we want to make as much profit as we can, and therefore to obtain as much business as we can reasonably handle. We want that business to be as profitable as possible. We spend as little as possible in obtaining it. And in order to develop a stable, sustainable business, we must limit our fixed overhead costs, balance our business risks with the opportunities they create, and minimise the duration between incurring costs and getting paid.

Within the limits of what we are set up to do, we have a great deal of freedom to decide what our 'products' are. But in the great world outside, numerous individuals and companies are deciding for themselves what *their* needs and problems are. On the basis of those needs, they are making their own decisions to buy. It is therefore always easier to adjust our products (as we call what we provide, be they conventional 'products' or 'services') than it is to persuade customers to adjust their needs. Our motto must be:

> We must make what we know we can sell. We must not try to sell only what we happen to make.

Creating a marketing strategy is an iterative process. We make some assumptions and test them; if they work well, we push on, if not, we try again. Our first step is to decide what business we are in.

What business are we in?

Are we builders? Are we architects? Are we ceiling tile manufacturers? Are we a one stop shop for everything that a building-owner might need? For marketing purposes, we must define our business in terms of what our customers really buy from us. On Sunday morning, the newsagent hands us a kilogram of newsprint. We have little use for newsprint. We buy the news, opinion, information and entertainment that the paper carries. The newspaper proprietor and the newsagent are in the business of selling those intangible commodities, not the physical newspaper *per se*.

Think about the business of being an architect. What does the architect's client buy? Not the building; buildings are bought from developers and existing owners. The design of a building? In exceptional cases, perhaps. But the design itself would be the principal product only where the client gave a brief at the first meeting and took little more part in the matter until the design was complete. In general, an architect's client buys a wide-ranging service which helps him to realise his idea for a building. The actual design is one of the results of the service. In turn, the physical building is the result of others using the design as a basis for providing their service. The architect, therefore, is in the business of providing a range of professional services which help the client to realise an idea for a building.

A clear understanding of the nature of our business is the first step in considering our marketing strategy. We have seen the need to 'place ourselves in the position of the customer'. Here we must do so in order to understand what the client thinks he is buying, so that we can define our products and shape our efforts to sell them.

A few, mostly quite eminent, architects are in the business of selling designs. Their clients know their reputation for creating magnificent buildings, and are not put off by competitors' warnings about the alleged pain of working with such an architect. Such a business succeeds for the few: most clients, however, look to their architect for a systematic, sympathetic, competent analysis of their needs and a reasonably creative but practical translation of the resulting brief into an economic and workable design. So an architect can be in at least two businesses: The 'design vendor' business, and the more common 'service vendor' business. Of course there is every shade between the two. Each will attract its own kind of client. In marketing terms, therefore, we are each in the business of providing what our customer sees or visualises when he decides to buy from us.

The elements of the strategy

Before considering the process of creating a marketing strategy, it will be helpful to look at some of the concepts involved. In doing so, we shall define the necessary specialist marketing terms. This volume aims to present marketing in a readily understandable construction industry context; readers who wish to study marketing in general more deeply are again referred to the recommendations for further reading at the end of the book. In particular, John Wilmshurst's *The fundamentals and practice of marketing*, one of the definitive text books for the Chartered Institute of Marketing professional qualification, gives a more detailed explanation of these concepts and their application.

Business objectives

Objectives must be set by the business unit, whether it is an independent organisation or a subsidiary within a larger group. These may be expressed in financial terms of turnover and profit, or quantitatively in terms of market share, number and size of projects, numbers of people and so on. They may also be expressed in terms of qualitative goals, such as the satisfactory establishment of certain activities, achieving quality assurance registration and the like. Most corporate strategies will contain objectives in each of these categories. Objectives are what must be achieved, as opposed to aims, which are statements of the more general direction of the business. For example: our aim is to become the market leader in our business sector; our objective for this year is to secure 10% of the United Kingdom business.

Products

For present purposes, we can define a product as the item that a customer buys. As we have seen, the idea of the product in the customer's mind may not be the same as its physical substance, and different kinds of customer may have a different idea of the same product. Take a 25 kg bag of lawn seed. Mother may see it as a perfect lawn, green through the summer, soft underfoot and with elegant straight mower stripes running from the patio to the boundary fence. Father may see it as a delicate paper sack to carry home, an uncomfortable couple of months keeping the birds off the garden and a weekly chore of mowing for the rest of his natural life. To sell it to the couple, we must recognise those different ideas and prepare selling messages accordingly. We are dealing here mainly with the marketing of 'services', i.e. things that are done for, rather than handed to, the customer. For marketing purposes we shall nevertheless call them products. Service products are less easy to describe than physical products: chapter 3 deals at greater length with their identification.

Product life cycle

New products may cost a great deal to develop and introduce, and then take some time to be accepted in the market and to achieve worthwhile sales volumes. They involve the risk of not succeeding. If they do succeed, competitors take up the idea and introduce similar or improved products. The market is finite, and however successful the product may be, it reaches maturity and its further growth is limited. A saturation point is reached at which everyone likely to use the product is doing so. Inevitably, the innovative, competitive market moves on, leading to the eventual decline of the product. This cycle of introduction, growth, maturity, saturation and decline is used to decide on the marketing action appropriate to support each product at each stage. The product life cycle concept recognises different types of customer, with propensities to buy a product at the various stages of its cycle. These types include 'innovators' who will try anything new; 'early adopters' who are quick to recognise a good thing when it is visible and respectable in the market; an 'early majority' and 'late majority' who, like most of us, buy tried and tested products but avoid the risks of too-early purchase; and finally the 'laggards' who are the very last to adopt the new product. This analysis applies equally, of course, to consumers and to companies. The cycle is an important reminder that in a live, competitive market, old products do not last forever; they must be carefully managed during their lifetime and eventually replaced with new ones.

Product portfolio analysis

A business offering a range of products must ensure that the range is balanced within the business and that there is a rational basis for allocating resources such as cash, research and development and sales effort between the products. The Boston matrix (or Boston box) is a technique that plots market growth against market share. Market growth is an important factor because new opportunities can be taken to satisfy the increasing demand present in a growing market. Our share of the market is significant because it determines the extent to which we can control the market or take advantage of it. Products are labelled 'star' if they enjoy a high share of a growing market; 'dog' if they are in a low growth market and have a minor share. A low growth/high share product may be a long-established product on which a great deal of marketing effort has been spent in the past to achieve the market share; it may now be known as a 'cash cow' because little effort is needed to sustain a good positive cash flow from it. The low share of growing market product is a 'problem child' (sometimes called a 'question mark' or a 'wildcat').

Stars are the front running products of the business. They represent profit and cash flow but require a lot of attention. Dogs are unexciting and neutral. The cash cows are mature products that no effort in the world will improve; the only thing to do is to take advantage of them while they are there. The problem child is where a great deal of attention is needed. Low share of a growing market means that there may well be everything to play for—but only if the product is good and likely to succeed. Too many stars mean that the company may be over-stretched. Too many dogs suggest that it may be dying on its feet. Cash cows feed the stars with cash, but a portfolio full of them suggests a tired company which has rested on its laurels and, because it is relatively inactive and cash rich, may be ripe for takeover. The problem child products are the ones that require a crystal ball. With effort and investment lavished on them, they may become tomorrow's stars.

It may be easier to see the application of the concepts of product life cycle and product portfolio analysis to the product range of a pharmaceutical company or a motor car manufacturer than to most construction industry situations. There are two reasons for this. First, most business units in the construction industry offer a limited range of discrete products. Second, our industry has not yet embraced the marketing culture to the extent that it thinks readily of the services it delivers as 'products'. Compare ourselves with the banking industry. Where is the friendly high street bank manager? He has been partially replaced by a team of young 'personal bankers' who sit at open desks on the customer side of the tellers' counter and offer a range of 'financial products'. Retail banking in the United Kingdom is now very competitive, and has become market-led. The construction industry will follow in this direction.

The new systems must provide better service than before. Our banks have some way to go to achieve that. By and large, we in the construction industry are only at the starting gate. But to understand our business and to shape our marketing strategy, we must recognise what our products are and where they stand within their own competitive marketplace. The question of product development is a study in itself, and further reading is recommended at the end of the book.

Packaging

In consumer goods, the packaging has become one of the most important vehicles for communicating selling messages to the buyer. The size and quality of the pack, and the images and messages printed on it, all say their piece. What respect do we have for half a dozen miserable steel screws lying on a counter? How much more attractive they are in a crisp, glossy bubble pack. Packaging intangible services is no less important and the term in this context means the way in which the set of services or scope of service, offered as a single product, are put together and described for the benefit of the customer.

Customers

A customer is someone who buys. A client is someone who receives a service which may have been bought or may be free. In particular, a customer receiving a professional or personal service is usually referred to as a client. For marketing purposes, we use the term 'customer' when contemplating everything to do with the buying process.

Repeat-order customers

In most businesses whose customers are in a position to come back for more, the existing clients are the most likely to provide future orders. Several stages in the selling process are already in place. We are in a position, by doing no more than providing a good service, to influence the customer's buying decision at a very early stage. Existing customers therefore enjoy a very high priority as targets for future business in most marketing strategies.

Competition

The existence of competitors, with their likely actions and reactions in the market, is a major factor in marketing strategy. And it is a factor which is easier to neglect in services marketing than where physical products can be seen on the shelves and in the showroom. We estimate the needs of potential customers. We must be aware of the competitors who aim to satisfy the same needs. In chapter 1 we described marketing as the recognition and use of the economic and other forces which exist within the market to create business. Our actions and the reactions of our competitors comprise one of the principal market forces. Therefore, knowing who our competitors are, their strengths and weaknesses, what they are doing and how they will respond to the things we plan to do, is essential to our strategic thinking. Our primary objective is to create profitable business. To do so, we must beat the competition. We may be obliged to beat them on price, on the quality of our product (which includes service, of course) or in other direct ways. But one of the purposes of spending time and money on preparing a marketing strategy is to identify areas in which the competition is weak, to which it does not have access or for which it will take a long time to prepare itself. If we can win the war without a battle, well and good!

Differentiation

We differentiate our product from its competitors by giving it or ascribing to it characteristics that they do not share. We put coloured stripes in the toothpaste. In the 1960s the gas industry used the phrase 'high speed gas' to differentiate its product from 'slower' alternative fuels. A go-ahead architect may differentiate his design and project management services by offering a formula for a guaranteed maximum price for the building contract.

Competitive differential advantage

If we can translate our differentiation into a real advantage over the competition, we have achieved a competitive differential advantage.

Pricing

In most sectors, products are priced at the level the market will bear. An estimate of cost is then made to determine what profit there is, and whether or not the product is viable. This is true of retail products, and it is certainly true of property development. In contracting, and to an increasing extent in professional services, we have become accustomed to cost-based pricing with the addition of a fine margin for profit and overheads. Contractors who provide undifferentiated services (a practice reinforced by competitive tendering with Bills of Quantity) earn undifferentiated margins. Contractors who offer something special, that other contractors cannot provide, to clients who can afford a high price, earn much better margins. In a market-led environment, pricing is not just a question of estimating the lowest price we dare submit.

Market sector

Construction is a major sector. A part of the economy within it there are other sectors such as building, civil engineering and repairs and maintenance. A definitive schedule of market sectors for the UK is given in the *Standard industrial classification (SIC)*, published as a booklet by HMSO. Its current edition divides economic activity into 10 divisions, 60 classes, 222 groups and 334 activity headings. This categorisation provides a valuable starting check-list and a useful framework for business-to-business marketing strategy. The term 'market sector' should not be confused with 'market segmentation', which is discussed below.

Fast-moving consumer goods (FMCG)

The initials 'FMCG', which are often a puzzle to people new to marketing, signify the large consumer marketing sector in which we are all customers. Because of its size and economic importance, this sector has been the main area for the development of marketing theory and practice.

Market size, market share

The size of a market is the annual amount of business it represents. Our market share is the percentage of the market that we have secured. For strategy purposes, it is important to be aware of these factors. The larger our share, the greater is our opportunity to dictate how the market behaves; the smaller our share, the weaker is our position, unless we have a competitive product that we can exploit to take business away from the dominant competitor. We also need to know whether the market size is increasing, standing still or decreasing; i.e. whether or not it is a growth market. In a growth market we can exploit new products or make an initial entry without having to displace dominant competitors.

Market research

Market research is the process of obtaining and evaluating information on the market. It includes the investigation of economic, political and social trends. Sample approaches to potential customers discover how they (and by implication others like them) will respond to our product offering, and their attitude to competitors. It will obtain details of competitors' offerings and competitors' business. Market research does not generally extend to the collection of information on individual potential customers; that activity is more likely to be thought of as sales information gathering.

Niche market

In architecture a niche is a small recess into which a work of sculpture is fitted. We have a 'niche' market if we fit ourselves into a narrow speciality and aim to succeed because we specialise and there is little competition. Niche markets can be profitable, but we must watch for changes to which our narrow specialisation makes us vulnerable.

Marketing mix

The marketing mix is the set of factors that make the product attractive to the customer. It is often expressed as *the four Ps*—product, price, promotion and place. Various schools of thought add other factors; perhaps the most useful addition in our context is that of service. The customer will buy the right product if the price is right. Appropriate promotion further predisposes him to buy, but he can only do so if the product is made available in the place where it is needed. The product must be in the shop rather than in the warehouse. If our service customer is in Timbuktu, our resources in London may not do him, and hence us, much good.

Segmentation

Segmentation means the separation of customers into groups according to the products they are likely to buy and the messages that will predispose them to buy. Segmentation is a very important concept in marketing. If our marketing plan separates our target customers into groups with particular needs, we can devise the most effective approach for each group. It is segmentation which, for example, leads different branches of the same supermarket chain to stock different ranges of goods to appeal to the buying habits of the local populace. The socio-economic group that dominates a particular area will be conscious of the need for healthy eating and will tend to buy low calorie drinks, wholemeal bread and a lot of fruit and fresh vegetables. Another group will favour burgers, fish fingers and frozen chips. This aspect of merchandising goes beyond merely having the biggest shelf for what we sold most of last week. Study of the buying habits of the segmented customers means that special promotions and new products can be introduced selectively in particular stores. An engineering services contractor offering a design, procurement and installation service may segment its market between the non-technical building owner, the building owner with a small engineering department and the professional client who may be a building owner, a consulting engineer or a contractor. Each of these three is attracted by different aspects of the broadly similar service product, and by a different approach.

Positioning

Positioning, which may apply to an individual product or to an entire business, means concentrating on a particular segment or range of segments of the market. In retail clothing it may be a focus on the young, trendy high spender; on the above-average sized man; on the broad band of people who want inconspicuous value for money; and so on. A main contractor may be positioned to serve the client who wants quality and is willing to pay for it, for public sector tightly-priced competitive tenders with potential claim opportunities, or for industrial or property development work where the client relies on performance to time and agreed cost.

Analysis

We recognise the factors involved in the market. Their interaction must be considered so that we can determine the effect of the various possible strategies.

SWOT analysis

SWOT stand for 'strengths, weaknesses, opportunities and threats. A SWOT analysis is usually the first step in the preparation of a marketing strategy. From it, we can understand and plan to use our strengths to exploit opportunities. We can recognise and repair or avoid our weaknesses, and defend against or sidestep any known threats. It is easy to confuse strengths with opportunities and weaknesses with threats. Strengths and weaknesses are characteristics of our own organisation, i.e. internal matters which are to some extent under our own control. Opportunities and threats are external factors over which we have no direct control, but to which we can react to our own advantage.

Mission statement

A mission statement encapsulates the aims of the organisation in a few succinct sentences. Its intention is usually to motivate the staff. It may also be directed at customers to make them aware of the qualities of the company with which they are dealing. Whether to have a mission statement at all, and how to make it say more than that we are for the family and against sin, are matters which must have occupied many boards of directors for many hours!

Benefit

We take decisions to buy on the basis of the benefits we expect to gain from the product. What is in it for me? We must, as always, place ourselves in the position of the customer and recognise the benefits that will attract him. The benefit of buying a bicycle is that it provides a low cost means of transport. There may be additional benefits. It may provide us with leisure entertainment and a feeling of well-being if we use it for physical exercise. It may give us social status if it is the kind of machine currently coveted by our peers. Different individuals may perceive different benefits from the same product. The 'features' of the product are not of direct relevance to the buying decision. One feature of a modern bicycle may be that it has 21 different gear ratios. We do not buy 21 gears. What we do buy is the benefit of being able to ride with ease on steep, rough terrain, the pride of possession of a machine so equipped, or the good feeling we gain from the envy of our contemporaries. Explaining benefits to particular audiences is a matter for some care. We must always understand the benefits, and then describe them as the buyer will perceive them. One type of marketing wisdom insists that we should not offer features at all, but concentrate on describing the benefits. We must remember that a sophisticated audience such as the professional buyers of construction services may know only too well the benefits that flow from certain features of the service. The teenager looking for a new bicycle is a sophisticated audience. We must predict the envy of friends. We must describe the pleasure of riding up a mountain—but we must not forget to say that there are 21 gears!

Selling argument

The case to be put to a particular customer group to convince them to buy a particular product. The selling argument is an essential link between the marketing strategy and the sales activity. The strategy defines the product, the customer, and the message we are going to communicate to the customer to make him buy. That message is the selling argument.

Unique selling proposition (USP)

This is a unique feature or argument for selling a particular product. Our product's USP is the characteristic which, in the mind of the customer, it shares with no competing product. A good example of USP in the UK construction industry is the Bovis Fee Contract, which was

Table 1. Possible list of headings for preparing a marketing strategy

Plan	Plan for preparing the strategy
Data collection and assembly	SWOT analysis What business are we in? Products Customers Competitors Resources Volume, pricing and profit External factors
Analysis	Key factors influencing the strategy
Strategy for customers and products	Positioning Segmentation Products Customers Selling arguments Pricing Volume and market share
Action, organisation, resources and budget	Sales strategy Organisation Budget The marketing action plan Arrangements for review

represented as unique in that it placed the contractor wholly on the side of the client as a member of his team.

Preparing the marketing strategy

Having outlined the concepts, we can now deal with the process of preparing the marketing strategy. Once again, our intention in preparing a marketing strategy is to have a carefully reasoned plan which tells us where our best customers are, what we should be offering them, how we should approach them and what we should be saying to them to convince them to buy from us rather than our competitors.

The detail of preparing the strategy will vary according to the nature of our business and whether or not we are starting systematic market planning from scratch. The possible list of headings for preparing a marketing strategy given in Table 1 is offered as a general guide, not as a universal model. However, the principles and techniques involved will be common to most strategies.

The headings may also form an activity list on which a plan for preparing the strategy can be based. Experience suggests that we should follow this kind of sequence, at first writing down tentatively what we can easily discover or decide. If we then make a further pass through the whole process, what we have discovered can be fed back to refine our thinking, to fill in gaps and to suggest additional work to improve the exercise. It may take several cycles before we achieve a credible strategy.

In summary, the process can be as follows. We first take stock of the things we are good at and those we are not good at, and of the external factors that may help or hinder us. We then take a broad view of our business, and decide what we believe to be its thrust and overall ambit. (In other words, we decide what business we are in.) The next stage is to examine, classify and record our products, customers, competitors and resources, and the factors affecting how much we sell, at what price and with what effect on profitability. Now we have a picture of the business, on the basis of which we can isolate the key factors that influence our strategy. We then proceed to develop the strategy on the basis of those factors. It is essential to remember that this schedule is merely an illustration of the principles involved: the most effective technique will be different for every business.

Plan

Plan for preparing the strategy

The suggested layout for the strategy represents a logical sequence for the argument which says what we are and what we can do, who our potential customers and competitors are, what we think we can sell most profitably and how we intend to proceed. The process of creating the strategy will probably follow the same sequence. The first step is therefore to decide on the headings for the eventual strategy document, and to draw up a programme for preparing it with firmly allocated responsibilities.

Data collection and assembly

SWOT analysis

Views within the organisation will differ regarding strengths, weaknesses, opportunities and threats. This starting point for the preparation of the marketing strategy is an opportunity to involve an appropriate group in a team exercise and to obtain a consensus if possible. We must be realistic, and ensure that our SWOT analysis represents what we are rather than what we would like to be.

What business are we in?

This part of the exercise defines the broad boundaries of our future business. It can be undertaken on the basis of our general knowledge of the existing business, in the light of the SWOT analysis, and will dictate the type and range of products we consider offering. It makes the first suggestion about the positioning of the company as a whole within its chosen sector. At appropriate stages in the further preparation of the strategy, we should look back at this statement to check that it remains valid.

Products

Chapter 3 deals in more detail with the identification and description of service products. A 'service product' is a clearly identifiable set of services which the client will recognise and buy. For example, each phase of an architect's or consulting engineer's professional engagement might be thought of as a separate product—inception, studies, design, documentation, working drawings, supervision and so on. Alternatively, the whole comprehensive service could be a single product. The contractor's traditional product could be defined as 'that service which fulfils the obligations of the Contractor under a JCT, ICE or other third-party contract'. 'New' products could be professional services such as technical audits, or contractor's services such as construction management.

At this stage in the preparation of the strategy, we must consider the existing activities of the business. If they are already classified as discrete products we must decide whether or not the classification is still valid from the customer's point of view. If we have not previously thought in terms of 'products', we must now think carefully about what our customers buy from us, and define our products accordingly. We must also begin to think of the new products we could be adding to our range, or new ways of packaging our existing activities to create new products. In the first iteration, we should be concerned mainly with existing products; ideas for new products can be developed more fully in later stages of the strategy.

Customers

This is the core of the strategy. Marketing is 'the management process responsible for identifying, anticipating and satisfying customer requirements profitably'. The whole business depends on customer requirements. We must schedule all our existing customers and find a basis for classifying them. The schedule must show the kind of customers they are, which products they buy, why they buy them from us and, as far as possible, the relative profitability to us of their business. It is not possible to suggest a single format for classifying customers for all businesses: the topic is discussed further in chapter 3. Our aim is to set down a clear customer–product matrix which will give us an indication of the way forward when we come to the analysis. That matrix will be different for each business.

Competitors

Competitors are a fact of life. They are people like us, using similar skills and techniques to try to obtain the same business. In preparing our own marketing strategy, we need to know as much as we can about theirs. What are they offering? What have we learned in competing with them? How do prices compare? Do they have any clever ploys for sidelining us at an early stage, to leave the field clear for them? And so on. We may consider individual competitors or categories of competitor, depending on the nature of the market.

Resources

What limitations do the quality, quantity and location of our human and other resources place on our ability to deliver our products on time, within cost and to the required standard? Which of these limitations can be overcome, and which must we take into account in shaping our strategy?

Volume, pricing and profit

In thinking about products, customers, competitors and resources we must remember that our objective is to 'satisfy customer needs profitably'. We shall only do so if individual items of business earn more than they cost to fulfil. And there must be enough of them for their profit contributions to exceed overhead costs (one of which is the cost of marketing). Either as a separate element of data collection, as set out here, or as part of the matrix of information about our market, we must note any information we have on volumes, pricing and historic profitability.

External factors

Up to this point we have been concerned mainly with our own experience of business in existing markets. We must now consider the broader factors of the marketplace. These include national and international economic and political factors, interest rates and currency values, trading conditions within the sectors we serve, developments and trends in our potential customers' use of their buildings, and developments in our own industry. One essential element is the market size of each sector we are interested in and an idea of its future growth prospects; this may be obtainable directly from statistics or by inference from economic and other factors. As before, we must remember what we are doing and why. If we write down a statement of external factors, it must be a clear statement of things that affect our business, not a thesis for a PhD in economics.

It is very important to remember that the purpose of assembling all this information is to use it to work out the best strategy for obtaining new business. An enormous volume of amorphous data will tell us nothing. We need selected data, presented in a form that allows us to see the wood as well as the trees. We cannot calculate a strategy, we can only arrive at it by a complex process of management judgements based on the best facts we can muster. This is not an academic exercise; it is a commercial one, and it requires information of commercial quality.

Analysis

Key factors influencing the strategy

This section is the interface between the collection of information and the formulation of strategy. It is now that we shall see how effective our classification of customers and products has been. Let us recall yet again that our intention in preparing a marketing strategy is to provide ourselves with a carefully reasoned plan which tells us

- where our best customers are
- what we should be offering them
- how we should approach them
- what we should be saying to them to convince them to buy from us rather than our competitors.

At this point in the first iteration of the process we should have a clear picture of what we are doing already, and of which combinations of product and customer are profitable and which are not. We should also have a first outline of how such external factors as the economy, fashions, and technological developments are likely to affect our markets. This section does not aim to be the strategy itself, but rather to crystallise all the information in a format that will make the strategy easy to develop. We pick out the key factors.

Having identified our first set of key factors, we may go straight ahead and draw up our first draft strategy, or we may choose to review the data collection exercise to test the sensitivity of our information and assumptions. Each cycle of the exercise should engender new ideas for products and customers.

Strategy for customers and products

This is the marketing strategy. Its structure and layout depend on the nature of the business, but it will contain statements on the following aspects of our strategy. The headings may not be shown separately, or may be shown in a different order.

Positioning

Which parts of our chosen market sectors do we aim to serve, and how do we present ourselves to them?

Segmentation

How do we divide our customers and products to enable us to plan our marketing efforts most effectively?

Products

We list our products.

Customers

We describe our target customers.

Selling arguments

What case shall we put in each segment?

Pricing

What is our pricing policy, as it affects our efforts to obtain business?

Volume and market share

How much business do we expect to acquire in each segment, and in what time-scale?

Action, organisation, resources and budget

Sales strategy

We have stated what we are going to offer to each kind of customer, and what we believe we should say to convince them. We now need to write down how we are going to do it!

Organisation

Marketing is not an activity confined to the marketing department. The marketing strategy must not only show how the dedicated marketing function is organised, but also the other parts of the organisation that share its aims.

Budget

What we have outlined so far is all good stuff, but can we afford it? The marketing budget should be related to the gross margins that the various segments can earn and, of course, to a realistic assessment of the likely business volume. The proportion of the margin we can afford for marketing depends on the size of the margin and the demands made of it by other overheads. There are no standards to go by, but for a significant proportion of construction-related businesses, marketing costs between one and two percent of turnover. Everything that anyone plans to do for the purpose of getting new business should be reflected in the marketing budget. This budget is likely to include, in parentheses, items from budgets of departments other than the marketing department. One such item may well be the cost of technical work undertaken at our own risk, which may become abortive. Whether this cost is recorded by the hour, or by making an allowance in the cost rate, it must be controlled and accounted for. It is important that we know what we are spending to get new business. Possible headings for the marketing budget are given in Table 2.

In developing our marketing strategy, if the marketing costs for a particular segment look like taking up more of that segment's gross margin than we can afford, we must recycle the plan to try to find another way, or reconsider the viability of that segment.

The marketing action plan

The real end product is the action plan, a detailed schedule of all we intend to do to implement our marketing strategy. Everything we have done so far has been in preparation for this plan.

Table 2. Possible headings for a marketing budget

Direct costs of dedicated marketing staff
Salaries
    Other salary-related costs
    Hotels, fares and meals
    Vehicle expenses
    Entertaining

Training

Corporate entertaining

Publicity
    Advertising
        Press
        Journals
        Television
        Other
    Literature and brochures
    Design costs
    Display materials
    Giveaways

Conferences and exhibitions

Market research and information

Public relations

Sponsorship

(Speculative professional costs)

Arrangements for review

The marketing strategy should contain procedures for monitoring its application, for periodic review and for a response to future external or internal changes that may require its alteration: suggestions are made in chapter 11. The plan for preparing the strategy must allow for review and approval at appropriate points to ensure that all levels of management accept the strategy and will act on it.

Keeping the balance: the danger of analysis-paralysis!

As we have seen, the systematic preparation and implementation of a logical marketing strategy is the core of a successful marketing programme. And a successful marketing programme is, of course, the central pillar of any successful business.

But we must keep the analytical activity in perspective. It is all too easy to allow data collection, market research and analysis to become ends in themselves. They are the tools of the job. Analysis is of value only as a source of information on which to base decisions. Many entrepreneurs succeed in business without a single page of formal research and analysis. But no business has ever succeeded on analysis alone!

3. Markets, products and competition

This chapter deals in greater depth with the principal components of the strategy: positioning and identity, recognition of market need, identification of products, selecting profitable combinations of product and customers, market segmentation, differentiation, selling messages and the action plan.

Positioning

Positioning means concentrating on particular segments of the market, i.e. groups of customers and products which can be the subject of a common approach. It also means making this concentration known. Positioning is required not only to limit the range and style of the business to areas in which we know we can succeed, but also to give the customer a clear understanding of the organisation and what it is offering. We are concerned about the impression given to our customers by the range of things we do.

Take, for example, a business hiring out cars with drivers. The customers for car hire are companies of all kinds and sizes and private individuals of every possible status. The vehicles may range from Mercedes limousines to owner-driver Vauxhall Cavaliers of a certain age. The drivers match their cars, from neatly pressed grey suit and grey cap to bomber-jacket-and-jeans part-timers. In most circumstances, it would be difficult to run a business that covered the whole range. The culture span is too great. The idea of the quality and comfort the limousine customer buys may be destroyed by the appearance of a minicab. Doubts may be cast on the economy of the minicab business if occasionally a Granada stretch turns up to deliver a parcel. This is a particularly interesting example, because the same customer buys at both ends of the market. The company sends a limousine to the airport to collect a foreign visitor; it calls a minicab to deliver a parcel or to take staff home in the silent hours. Individuals take a minicab home from the pub; they may hire a limousine for a family wedding or for a special night out. The customary positioning options are for either the 'limousine' business or the 'minicab' business.

A local building business may, for example, comprise four profitable activities: high quality shopfitting, cabinet-making, in situ timber treatment and preservation, and drain cleaning. These are four perfectly respectable activities, each profitable and each with a good reputation in its field. From a production point of view, they are perfectly compatible: they share premises quite comfortably and enjoy the support of a range of common services. But from a marketing point of view, it is very difficult to give outsiders an attractive idea of what the four activities together stand for. Shopfitting requires a combination of good specialist design, high-quality workmanship and a rather special approach to site work in live retail premises; the customers are the retailers and the professionals who serve them. Cabinet-making involves very high quality joinery work; the customers are architects, main building contractors and other shopfitting contractors. In situ timber treatment is at the 'dirty overalls' end of the business. It may have grown out of a general building activity which served shopkeepers, but the customer with high-quality fitted joinery in mind does not want to think of men in wellies with injection pumps near his work. And as for rodding the drains...!

The answer to the positioning question in this case is probably to show the world two separate pairs of activities. The shopfitting and cabinet-making fit well together and complement one another. Shopfitting gives cabinet-making an image of speedy response; cabinet-making lends shopfitting a feeling of high standards and special attention. Together they can be positioned for quality and service to customers who need it, appreciate it and can afford it. On the other hand, the two 'overalls and wellies' businesses also fit well together, positioned to provide a service to building owners, public and private, in looking after the parts of the estate that other, more 'respectable' firms do not wish to reach.

Positioning is the major part of deciding what business we are in. As such, it is one of the key decisions of our marketing strategy.

Image and identity

Our 'image' is the idea that our customers, the general public and other audiences have of our organisation. In another sense, it is the one we would like them to have. Our 'corporate identity' is a policy for the appearance of all the physical manifestations of the organisation, designed to project an appropriate image. We intend that our image and our corporate identity should support our marketing and other ambitions. Chapter 7 deals in some detail with corporate identity. We must remember the German folk tale of Rumpelstiltskin, which tells of the consequences of the king discovering as untrue his father-in-law's claims that his young bride could spin straw into gold. The fairy-tale has a happy ending, but our business is not a fairy-tale and we must not over-promise by trying to project an image that we cannot follow through.

Recognition of market need

In marketing, the prize goes to the lateral thinker. Anyone with a little nous can judge the market by what other people are selling successfully and can offer a similar, perhaps marginally improved, product in competition. Marketing people call these 'me too' products. There is plenty of room for them if the market is big enough and growing; after all, not everyone can be a leader in every product all the time. But to be really successful, we must try to be one jump ahead.

Consumer products satisfy the needs of individuals. Some of those needs existed long before marketing was thought of, others were created by the introduction of the product. The vacuum cleaner was invented to satisfy a recognised need for a more efficient way of cleaning floors. Its sales grew with the social and economic development which meant that fewer people were willing or available to spend the day on their knees with a dustpan and brush. They grew again as wall-to-wall fitted carpets became the rule rather than the exception.

Television is an example of a need created by the product that satisfies it. Before television became widely available in the 1940s and 1950s, entertainment of a similar kind was provided by the cinema. Many families and individuals made several visits to the cinema each week. News and other information was provided by newspapers and radio. In the 1940s a television set was something of a curiosity, able to receive just a single BBC channel in black and white. Just a few decades later, everyone in the western world 'needs' a television set. In the early 1990s, with the spread of cable and satellite TV and the growing availability of recorded films for hire in high-street shops, TV and video have become a very significant consumer market.

The equivalent commercial 'need' created by the technological revolution is for computers. What business needed an electronic digital computer in 1950? The development of data handling power and its delivery to the desk top, where thousands of people have it literally at their fingertips, has created opportunities for business, banking, medicine and government to handle and use information in ways that were never dreamed of in the days of clerks, ledgers and manual typewriters.

Most of us will not invent products like the vacuum cleaner, television or the computer! However, in our own marketing we must focus our minds on what our potential customers may need. We must place ourselves in the position of the customer and see what his problems are. Think of our own experiences with customers. In what areas have there been uncomfortable moments? Are these symptoms of a need for some different or better service that we could readily adjust ourselves to provide? What are the grumbles about our sector of the construction industry? Go and talk to a few regular customers of our sector. If they had one wish for better service from our industry, what would it be? Most concerns fall under one of three headings: quality, cost and time. What do our customers need in each of these that they are not getting now? And how can we adjust what we do, or do something new within our range of competence, to satisfy these unfulfilled needs?

Identification of products

Why do we now have to identify as 'products' the perfectly ordinary things we have always done for our clients? What was the matter with simply being an architect or an engineer and providing the range of services normally associated with the profession? As a contractor, we have always responded to the wishes of the professionals and their clients, we understand the different forms of contract, and we use our commercial muscle on site to get the best performance for the client. How can all that become a product? As a building component supplier, our windows or doors are our product; what more is there to consider?

As long as we follow the traditional systems and are content to accept the share of the available business that falls to us, we are perfectly entitled to think of our services in this vague sort of way. But if we want to expand our business and make it more profitable, and in doing so make the organisation and its people more secure, we must organise ourselves to present what we do in a much clearer and more positive light. We must identify what the customer actually buys before we can set about selling it to him.

Let us look back to the example of the friendly neighbourhood bank manager. He sat at his office in the high street, taking deposits from those of us who were lucky (or prudent) enough to have more money than we could keep under the mattress. He sat and waited until the rest of us, who did not have any money, came along to ask for an overdraft or a loan. The bank operated in a way that suited itself. It had to protect its own position and the funds of its depositors. It knew from experience, and from the conditions under which it accepted deposits and made loans, just how much money it had to have available for the immediate use of its customers, and how much it could afford to invest profitably elsewhere. It was an operations-based system, with little need to take account of the finer points of its customers' needs. Worldwide deregulation of the banking system has changed all that. The retail banks now compete with

40

a whole range of other institutions—building societies, insurance companies, the Post Office, retail stores—to provide consumers with various kinds of financial service. In order to compete with these inter-lopers, the high street bank now takes great care to understand the probable needs of the various kinds of customer. A means of satisfying each need is carefully designed and the price calculated and quoted; the terms and conditions are printed on the back of the leaflet. Current account, interest-bearing current account, personal loan, life assurance, life insurance, personal pension, buying and selling shares, PEP, TESSA: a whole range of 'products' rather than a high street financial entrepre-neur behind his desk having to decide whether the customer is a good risk or not. The products are defined. The bank is now selling hard to the customer.

The construction industry used to be made up of architects, engineers, quantity surveyors, builders, contractors, subcontractors, suppliers and manufacturers, all of whom did their own thing. Like the banking industry, the whole show was organised to suit its own operational needs rather than the needs of the customer. In our oft-repeated phrase, we must 'place ourselves in the position of the customer'. If we think carefully about what it is that the customer buys, we can formulate products suited to his needs.

We look first at the building owner-occupier who is the archetypical customer for the building industry. Think of the process he may go through to create a new building. The first step is to define his own need. This requires some sort of analysis of the activity and the people or activities to be accommodated. That need is to be translated into a building brief. If the client does not already have a site, the location is decided and a site acquired. Funding is raised by one of the many routes available. The project team is selected and appointed. Initial designs and estimates of cost and time are prepared. Outline planning consent is obtained. Designs are developed and co-ordinated. Prices and pro-grammes are decided and contracts placed within whatever contracting structure has been agreed. Physical work of various kinds is put in hand. Cost and time is managed and reported on. Quality is monitored on site. The building is commissioned. It is handed over to the client who moves his activities into it. If we look in more detail at the complex process this brief outline represents, we shall recognise our own part in it, as seen by our client, and how it relates to that client's actual needs.

In office politics, some individuals focus strongly on the need to be well thought of by the boss, and they sometimes succeed. In marketing our services, we must similarly focus on the client. The client takes the decisions about who will do what in the project. We need to analyse the process, understanding the point of view of our client at each stage. We can then formulate 'products' which are packages of our service designed specifically to suit the needs of the customer. At certain phases of the project, the client will wish to proceed to a particular stage and then pause before taking the next decision. Our 'product' will be particularly attractive if it takes that need into account, and does not try to commit the client beyond the point to which he is already committed to the project. We shall, of course, try to create a situation in which we are likely to be the most favoured contender for the next stage! Some examples of products offered by various types of construction industry organisation will illustrate this point.

The architect's main product is a comprehensive service to realise the client's concept for a new or altered building. This is a well established product; the world at large understands that this is what an architect provides. But an architectural practice may find disadvantages in concentrating on that global product alone. Does it suit the customer's need? And is it differentiated from the products offered by competitors?

Few client organisations are certain from the outset that they are going to proceed with the idea they have for a building. Will it work? How long will it take to reach completion? What will it cost? Will it fit on the site? The client needs some advice before making a commitment to the full services of the architect. Clearly-defined advisory services are therefore a particularly attractive product and, from the architect's point of view, they represent a very important opportunity to get alongside the client on day one, and to become indispensable for the later stages of the project. This idea is by no means a new one, but in our systematic attempts to obtain new work, which we call 'marketing', we should think of the 'front end' advisory services package as a product that can be promoted to clients who need it, by stressing the real benefits of accepting our particular package of service on our particular terms.

The second question is whether or not the individual architect's global service is differentiated from that of the many other firms which offer the same professional plan of work. Each firm is different from all others. Each has its strengths and its particular experience. What are we good at? What are the special bees in the bonnets of the kind of clients we best serve? If we are particularly good at cost management, we may consider arranging our services into a product package which offers some sort of guarantee of the cost of the finished building—with risks carefully calculated and with the specific agreement of our professional indemnity insurers! Do we have a special track record in project management? Should we offer that as a separate product? If our partnership resulted from a 'spin-out' of the design team from a regional health authority, can we offer a product that recognises the complex procedures for briefing, designing and gaining approval and funding for National Health Service projects? And so on. We may offer a range of products or concentrate on just a few.

The consulting structural or building services engineer, who has chosen to regard the architectural profession as a main source of business, is in a slightly different position. The needs of both the immediate and the ultimate client can be taken into account. One of the main needs of the architect is to get work from building owners. What special service can the consulting engineer offer to the architect which will help them both to get work? Very important criteria for considering a service product are: 'Will it help the immediate customer to get more business? Will it help the customer in achieving other important business objectives?' In these 'green' days, the offer of energy efficiency is always a good idea. Are there specialist structural services that will strike a chord with architect, client or both? Can we identify the cause of building vibrations which affect VDUs, and eliminate them or reassure the users? Do we have special knowledge which would give the client confidence in the design team for a range of currently fashionable project types? Can we offer a package of CAD-based services which not only match those of the architect, but will also provide a basis for the client's facilities management activity?

The builder or main contractor's product range has become much broader in recent years. The traditional builder's key product used to be a service to translate the architect's design into a physical building under the terms and conditions of one of the standard forms of 'third party' contract. That continues to be very important product, but other products have evolved to suit modern needs. These are usually described by the form of contract or project structure within which they operate. As 'products', we can describe them as what the client buys when they are adopted. 'Design and build' can be described in the same terms as the architect's main product: 'a comprehensive service to realise the client's concept for a new or altered building'. We must add, however, that while the architect acts as contractual 'agent' for the client, the design-and-build contractor is a direct 'party' to the contract. For this and other reasons, the product offered to the client almost certainly differs from the 'professional' service offered by the traditional architect. Each design-and-build arrangement will be different and will offer its own range of benefits (and disadvantages), according to the firm or team offering it and the needs of the customer.

A growing range of management products are also now offered by contracting organisations: management contracting, construction management, design and management etc. The design-and-build and management products may be offered directly to the ultimate client, perhaps on the advice of intermediary professionals. In shaping the product we must consider to whom it is to be offered, and who will influence buying decisions. The benefits of the product must be designed for that class of customer and their advisers.

The contractor may also offer a range of advisory service products. As we saw for a consulting engineer, the contractor's 'front end' services may be used as a lever to obtain direct business, or as an opportunity to support other members of the construction team who will pass on the appropriate parts of any project they bring in.

A subcontractor, particularly one with specialist technical capability, can consider all the above kinds of service product and can shape them to offer to main contractors, professionals and the ultimate client alike. The energetic, market-led specialist subcontractor need not be the 'tail-end-Charlie' who waits on the rest of the industry both for new business and for payment. The opportunity for him to serve a multi-level clientele is considerable. For example, one of the greatest problems in complex, multi-serviced modern buildings is the dimensional co-ordination of engineering services that are designed by a host of specialist engineers and installed by a different matrix of contractors. The multi-service contractor who offers as his link product a really effective system of managing and policing the allocation of technical space and engineering services would really differentiate his service from that of his business competitors.

The physical products of materials or component suppliers are easier to recognise: for this reason, however, it may take more effort to remember to describe them and to consider their marketing in terms of how they are seen by the immediate customer. Is a double-glazed, hardwood framed, remote-controlled roof light with an integral sun blind just a window for letting in the light and air when we want them and keeping them out when we don't? Of course not: in a domestic loft conversion, or the refurbishment of an industrial building for use as an office or a theatre, it is a critical feature in creating an interesting and attractive design. The 'product' we sell is not necessarily just what we make; in marketing it is what the customer 'buys'.

We have so far assumed that the ultimate customer is an owner-occupier. An owner-occupier with in-house professionals is a different matter, as are a portfolio developer creating assets for investment and a trading developer creating assets to pre-fund, pre-let and sell on. Each of these requires a slightly different set of services. Then there are the many public sector clients. And so on.

Having sorted what we offer to our customers into a series of 'products' we must remind ourselves that we have done so to enable us to define what we are offering in terms of the customer's need. It is then possible to devise the approaches and the messages that will convince the customer to buy that product from us rather than a similar one from our competitor. We must take care in presenting our newly defined products. We must as always place ourselves in the position of the customer. The customer may welcome a service overtly described as a 'product', but we are much more likely to get a favourable response from a less visibly aggressive approach, keeping our 'marketing' to ourselves and simply offering a carefully separated and packaged range of services designed to meet the customer's needs.

Competition

People debate whether or not life exists on other planets in the universe. There are arguments for and arguments against. But if the question is whether or not there are other organisations who are capable of doing the same work as we are, and whether or not they are out there working as hard as we are to get it, there is no argument at all. Competition is a fact of life.

Everything we plan to do to seek new business must take into account what our competitors are likely to do. We can only take their likely actions into account if we know who they are, and take some trouble to find out what they are thinking of doing. Competitor information is dealt with in chapter 4.

Two senior colleagues in a well-known construction group were discussing their two subsidiary companies' approach to getting new work. The civil engineering contracting manager said to his colleague from the design-and-build side, 'Our job is to get on the tender list; your job is to make sure that there is no such thing as a tender list in the first place!' He thought he was comparing the nature of the two businesses, but in fact he was comparing their approach to marketing. Competing is not necessarily about full-frontal price war in a competitive tender. Competition is more like a game of chess in which moves are planned far ahead, and their consequences calculated with precision.

There is a simple hierarchy of competitive strategy where the competitive aim is to secure a contract. The order of priority is as follows.

(1) Avoid competition by ensuring that competitors are not even aware of the opportunity.
(2) If there is competition, try to arrange for it to take place on our favoured ground.
(3) If price competition is inevitable, use all available tactics to submit the offer that will be accepted, by submitting the lowest price or otherwise.

This concept is dealt with in greater depth in chapter 6; for the present we shall consider its implications for marketing strategy and planning.

To be aware of opportunities that are denied to our competitors, we must take trouble to find them. Using a fishing analogy again: our competitor may bring his rod and his stool to a sunny bend in the river where it is known that anglers are usually successful. We study the habits and habitat of our target fish, and know where, when and under what conditions they feed. We go down to the river before dawn and stake our claim on the bank while scattering some ground bait ready for feeding time. When the time comes, we are there, reeling them in while our competitor is enjoying the sunshine.

Our information, our efforts to find where our customers are, our positioning—whether on the river bank or in business—our bait, that is, our arguments to bring the customer to us, and our product itself must each be better than that of our competitor. Points (1)–(3) for avoiding competition, or at least making sure that the outcome is to our advantage, may seem antisocial. We must understand why this is not so.

Competition is a very important economic factor, which stimulates invention, development and efficiency. Freedom to compete and to benefit from the results of success in competition has contributed largely to the difference in economic standards between the East and West in the second half of the twentieth century. Because of the 'third party' structure of our traditional contracting arrangements, our construction industry has narrowed the concept of competition to that of competitive tendering on price. The industry and its customers are learning that this is not necessarily the most efficient form of competition.

The capital cost of a building may comprise, say, 20% design, management and other 'fee' costs and 80% construction costs. The design element may represent about half of the fee costs. The spread of serious construction tenders may be 10%. The cost of building the least efficient acceptable design offered by the design team may be 50% greater than that of the most efficient. On these assumptions, and looking at each component of the overall cost, some important lessons can be drawn about the economy of our industry. The greatest single determinant (at about 40%) of total cost is the efficiency of the design. The variation between lowest and highest contract tender is significant (8%) but smaller. Price competition for the design fee element may affect the total cost by 1%.

These facts contribute to the following arguments for using non-traditional project structures—arguments which are far from being antisocial.

● The greatest single determinant of overall value for money in construction is the efficiency of the design. This must be taken into account in the selection and appointment of the designers and in determining the structure within which they work. While value for money in fees is essential, excessive zeal in cutting fees may save less than it costs in design efficiency.

● Competitive tendering for construction, based on sound documentation and firm designs, forms the most usual basis for appointment of contractors and subcontractors. However, this is not the only means of even-handed selection and does not always result in the lowest price or the lowest final construction cost.

The buyer operates under economic forces, and will in general take buying decisions for economic reasons. Competition therefore has its greatest effect when brought to bear on the whole economic process of creating or altering a building.

Selecting profitable combinations of product and customer

The aim of our marketing activity is to obtain the greatest volume of the most profitable work available, using the least effort and expense. Within the broad definition of our business there are many different products we can offer to many kinds of customer. To achieve our marketing aim, we must select the combinations of products and customers with which we are most likely to succeed. There is no merit in selling ice-cream to eskimos if we can sell twice as much to Californians with half the effort!

To identify the 'ice cream' and the 'Californians' in our business, we must do what we can to analyse our own historical performance. The precision we can bring to bear on this analysis will depend on how good (and how relevant to this exercise) our management accounting records are. We must first create a matrix of existing customers and existing products. The format of the matrix must depend on the pattern of customers and products; in devising it we must keep in mind the aim of the exercise, which is to prioritise our approaches to each category of customer with each of our products.

Having recognised the basic customer/product pattern, we must add whatever data we have on profitability. From a marketing point of view, we are interested not only in the actual commercial profit we have made, but also in the cost of acquiring the work and the longer-term gains resulting from the acquisition of an individual contract. For example, a client likely to undertake a once-in-a-lifetime project is less 'profitable' than a potential repeat order customer. A client who is very difficult to approach, and with whom a relationship may require several years gestation before we have a chance of getting an order, is less 'profitable' than one who is easy to reach and will give a fairly short-term decision. A client who is similar to many others and who will provide experience, track record, reputation or other marketing advantage in relation to those others is more 'profitable' than the truly one-off customer. Because most of these factors cannot be expressed quantitatively, we are likely to rely on a ranking system for allocating priorities. We must remember that we are making informed judgements on the best information available rather than calculating a marketing policy.

Having undertaken this analysis for our existing customers and products, we can extrapolate it to make similar judgements about potential new customer groups and new products. The result will be a schedule of customers and the products they buy from us, with a clear indication of their relative attractiveness from a business point of view.

In thinking about the relative merits of combinations of product and customer, it is worth considering the question of risk. We know how our existing customers behave, and we can anticipate the problems that will arise in serving them. Our tried and tested products involve only risks that we understand and can manage. New customers and new products introduce new risks, of which we may not be aware. It is a well established piece of marketing wisdom that we should offer new products to existing customers and existing products to new customers, but approach a combination of new product and new customer with great caution.

Market segmentation

Having recognised and prioritised combinations of customers and products, we are in a position to segment our market. Segmentation, as we saw in chapter 2, means the separation of customers into groups according to the products they are likely to buy and the messages that will predispose them to buy. We do this so that our marketing efforts can be planned efficiently.

Take, as a simple example, a small provincial contracting group which undertakes medium-sized building and civil engineering contracts, and has a civil and structural design office and a small mechanical services contracting department which has evolved from the pumping and piping side of the civil engineering business. The firm has a reputation for quality and integrity, and for value for money rather than lowest prices. The main clientele are local government, health authorities, the utility undertakings and British Rail, who provide a steady flow of third-party contracts designed and documented by their in-house professionals. The local brewery, whose chief engineer is mainly concerned with the process activity, relies on the firm for a quick and capable response on a design-and-build basis for a wide range of building and minor civil engineering works. Several local architectural firms employ the civil and structural design office as a consulting engineer; they also obtain advice, designs and prices from the mechanical services section, leading to nominated subcontracts. The founder of the firm, who has built the business by being all things to all men, begins to reduce his personal involvement. Marketing is to be devolved to other managers and engineers. Segmentation is required as a basis for allocating responsibility.

The customers categorise neatly into public or near-public sector

48

with in-house professionals, private sector industrial customers and architects. The main products are third-party building and civil engineering contracting with design by others, design and construct, civil and structural design, and mechanical services with design. In this case the segmentation of customers should not cause much difficulty. The public sector clients buy the solid reliable building and civil engineering contracting services. The path to that business is to be seen to be solid and reliable and to get on the tender list. The brewery and the architects buy a design service, followed up by either building and civil engineering construction or mechanical services installation. The path to that work is to be technically responsive to the client's needs and to take care not to kill the goose that lays the golden egg of repeated negotiated contracts. There are therefore, in marketing terms, two clearly defined segments. It should not be difficult in that kind of contracting organisation to find two individuals with the necessary qualities to build and maintain customer relationships in one or other of the two segments.

Differentiation

In a market where all competitors provide a more or less standard product, we must differentiate our product from those of our competitors. We must endow it with qualities, real or apparent, that make it more attractive to the customer.

In consumer marketing, the example of 'pure' orange juice is often cited. Orange juice is evaporated into a concentrated form in the country of the fruit's origin, for economical bulk shipping around the world. The concentrate is traded and eventually delivered to a processing plant in or near the consumer's country, where it is diluted with treated water, sterilised by a UHT process and filled into the familiar patented brick packs which have a shelf life of many months without refrigeration. The processing plant may be owned by the 'brand' on the pack, or the brand may be one of many supplied under contract by the plant. With minor variations, the same product is sold with many different labels in supermarkets worldwide.

In chapter 2 we met the concept of the marketing mix which sells the product. The four elements of the mix are product, price, promotion and place. In three of the four we have little room for manoeuvre in marketing orange juice. The product is orange juice just like any other, there is little we can do to change the price, and as far as place is concerned, if it's not on the shelf in the supermarket we are not in the business. In this case, we are left with promotion to differentiate our orange juice product from the rest of the pack(s).

We cannot make a false claim that our orange juice is something the other identical products are not. We can, however, give it a brand name that suggests qualities the other brands do not emphasise, represent those qualities in the design of the pack, and promote the evocative brand name by media advertising, point-of-sale material and so on. The more or less identical product is therefore differentated. How far we should go in spending precious marketing budget in trying to differentiate our brand of orange juice is a matter for broader consideration. We saw in chapter 2 that in a low growth or static market, if we have a high market share we have a 'cash cow' and if we have a low share of the market we have a 'dog'. Neither position justifies massive spending on promotion. But we must remember that all such techniques for helping us to decide what to do about marketing are only there to inform our common-sense commercial judgements. Our competent competitors use the same techniques— those whose postition is similar to ours will be moved to similar action. We must not ignore opportunities for carefully considered maverick moves that buck the trend.

In the consumer sector there are many examples of this kind of differentiation by added-value promotion. As we turn into the supermarket aisle crowded with competing brands of cornflakes, can most of us honestly suggest that we are not influenced by the jingle which immediately comes to mind, 'Kelloggs cornflakes, sunshine breakfast . . .'? And does Heineken really refresh the parts that other beers cannot reach? We don't even have to believe it does, as long as we associate the brand name with the all-over refreshing feeling created by a long cool lager.

In the construction industry there is both the need and the opportunity for differentiation in marketing. Most of our products are very much the same across the board. If we want our own services to stand out and to be selected by potential customers we must find a way of differentiating them. The customer's buying decision is influenced, as we have seen, by the four elements of the marketing mix: product, price, promotion and place. We can use any one or all of them to differentiate our offering from that of our competitors. Let us consider each element in turn.

The 'product' means the actual qualities of the service product or physical product we offer—including its quality *per se*! We can differentiate by making changes to the product itself. If we are construction managers, we may offer an improved system of construction planning which gives the client greater confidence in progress reports. A foundation contractor may offer a new technique for testing piles during their formation, thereby saving the time and cost of in situ pile tests. The architect may re-equip the design office to provide three-dimensional CAD which gives the client walk-through experience of the building and feeds automatically into the quantity surveyor's taking off.

The 'price' may be the actual sum of money we ask for a particular piece of work, but it is more likely to represent a broader measure of the economic cost incurred by our customer as a result of our involvement. This definition of price is particularly relevant in the case of professional services. A firm of quantity surveyors which provides a really effective 'value engineering' service and an effective project cost management facility may save, or avoid the risk of, expenditure many times the direct fee cost of the service.

In the case of service products, 'promotion' means the sum of all the contacts, messages and information we convey to our potential customer through letters, meetings, our reputation on the industry's grapevine, advertising, trade literature and so on. As with orange juice, our most rewarding attempts at differentiation are likely to be here. The obvious place to start may seem to be in the marketing effort itself and, like the sunshine breakfast and refreshing of parts the others cannot reach, in how we describe our product. But in an industry not noted for taking great care of its customers, we must consider the whole way in which we relate to our clients, and the manner of the delivery of our service.

We do not have to 'make a better mousetrap'. We just have to give the impression at every point of contact that we are there only to serve our customer. The client's team must have the constant feeling, even when there are the inevitable matters for dispute, that it is a real pleasure to do business with us.

Finally, 'place' can be a significant factor: where our offices and depots are located, where we are willing to form a project team, where we hold stocks of materials, where our managers are based—all of these may contribute to our being seen by customers as offering something better than the others.

Selling messages

We have identified our potential customers. We have decided what products we plan to sell to them. We have even segmented the customers into groups according to the products they buy and their reasons for buying them. The latter is particularly important, because it gives us the clue to what we should be telling customers about the product to persuade them to buy it, i.e. the selling message.

Why do we buy a particular motor car? Different types of car appeal for different reasons to different kinds of people. The basic small car appeals to those who want convenient transport. The high performance small car is likely to be of interest to the young person who feels the need to extend his or her personality by the 'winning' performance of an economic small car. The station-wagon may represent convenient transport to a large family or to someone with a work or leisure need for the load space it contains. It may equally appeal, particularly if it has four-wheel drive, on account of its 'country' status. Expensive saloons may offer comfort, convenience, status and short journey times to those whose own or whose employer's purse can run to them. With the high performance large car, we come back to the extension of personality, but on a grander scale! Each reason for buying each kind of motor car requires its own selling message. We can see these various messages daily on television and in other media.

In any debate, argument or negotiation, we need to keep firmly in mind a simple set of basic facts on which our strategy is based. If everything we say is consistent with these facts, we offer a rational and coherent response to every argument or question put to us by the opposition. The same is true in marketing. For each segment of our market we must decide what is likely to convince a particular kind of customer or adviser and, for that segment, write down a set of selling messages. These messages then form a clear basis for the preparation of sales literature, advertising, sales letters, proposals, negotiations, in fact every communication we may have with our potential customer.

For example, consider a comprehensive project management service. Effective project management is to everyone's advantage, but the reason for that advantage may well be different for each of the various parties who influence the selection of our particular service. To the ultimate client, effective project management means the effective achievement of objectives of quality, cost and time. The main message must be that we ensure that achievement. Secondary messages may depend on the nature of the ultimate client: a once-off owner-occupier, a seasoned developer etc. The message to the architect who is already appointed may be that we will achieve the client's objectives but at the same time provide services to the design team that will make their work more efficient and more profitable. The quantity surveyor will need messages suggesting a positive relationship on the cost management side. The contractor will need to be reassured as to any potential conflict with the traditional management role of the main contractor.

These messages must be clearly recognised and recorded for use when required. And we must understand that there is no ethical or philosophical difficulty in saying different things to different parties, provided that the messages are consistent and not untrue. Remember that two people looking at a cylinder from the side and from the end will describe it as a rectangle and a circle. Both are right, even though neither has the full picture.

The action plan

All of the above is very well, but unless we put our marketing intentions into action in an orderly manner with proper mangement controls, our research, planning, analysis and strategies will be wasted.

The marketing strategy tells us where our customers are, what products we will offer them and what messages we will use to convince them. It tells us what we hope to achieve in terms of volumes, profits and market share. The marketing action plan tells us the who, when and how of putting the marketing strategy into action.

The precise format of the action plan depends on the organisation. But in essence it is a schedule of things that have to be done, with responsibility clearly allocated to individuals and departments and the time by which objectives must be achieved clearly set down. The plan must be agreed in advance with all the parties involved, who must be given the opportunity of acknowledging ownership of their part of it.

A suggested list of headings is given below, with some comments on what may be included under them. The plan must contain this kind of information, but remember that the format cannot be dictated without knowledge of the individual marketing strategy that underlies the plan.

Possible headings for marketing action plan

Marketing strategy—summary and objectives

Customers, Products, Segmentation, Business volume targets by market segment.

A synopsis of the strategy is included in order to make the action plan a self-contained document.

Organisation and responsibility

Outline organisation (dedicated marketing team; non-dedicated personnel), Responsibility for customers and products, Responsibility for other marketing-related activities.

This section shows both reporting lines and actual individual responsibility for all marketing and marketing-related work.

Campaign plans by market segment

This is the centrepiece of the action plan. In most cases, the campaigns will involve information assembly, approaches and relationship building with selected potential customers. The segments must be scheduled with a detailed plan for assembling information and making initial approaches. The more detailed this section of the action plan, the easier it will be to manage the resulting campaigns. Each plan must have a calendar dated programme attached to ensure that a pace is set and maintained and, in particular, that resource implications for the programme are clearly defined.

Press and publicity

Press relations, Other public relations, Advertising, Literature and brochures, Display materials, Giveaways, Sponsorship.

Each of these activities must be scheduled, with its aims clearly attached. Ony a small number should be labelled as general publicity or contingency. Unfocused press and publicity activities may be at best wasted, at worst counter-productive.

Corporate events

The aims must be clearly stated, and the event planned with its aims in mind.

Information and market research

Market research and information gathering are two separate topics. The latter is on-going, day in and day out, as we shall see in chapter 4. The need for formal market research must be carefully considered, and plans made as appropriate.

Training

There is a need for development training for specialist staff, whose skills must be kept up to date with modern advances. In the construction industry, where professional staff are inevitably involved in marketing, and indeed may transfer from technical and general managerial roles into formal marketing, there is a need for training in basic marketing skills. Many organisations also find that as they begin to adopt a marketing culture, cultural training for surprising numbers of management and professional staff is required.

Marketing budget

In the end, it all has to be paid for. Incorporating a copy of the budget as part of the action plan is essential, as the purpose of the marketing budget is to pay for the marketing action plan!

4. Information

The importance of information

James Boswell wrote in his *Life of Samuel Johnson*, published in 1791:

Knowledge is of two kinds. We know a subject ourselves, or we know where we can find information upon it.

These two kinds of knowledge are essential elements of marketing. We must collect and store information about our customers, about the markets they represent for us, about our competitors and our own activities in relation to them. And, we must develop systems and networks which ensure that when we need new information, the means of obtaining it is already in place and does not have to be invented.

In the early 1990s, we may be at the height of the information revolution. Our problem is not of obtaining information and handling it, but of making sure that we have the information we most need and that we can retrieve it in a usable form when we need it.

Marketing is about achieving and managing business relationships. The relationship may centre on what is no more than a simple across-the-counter transaction. But in the construction industry, most relationships involve the provision of services over a period of time. These services are delivered within a complex structure of client and project teams. From project to project, the teams form and disperse. Today's joint venture partner is tomorrow's competitor—or even today's! To know where to look for suitable customer relationships, to understand the customer and know what approach will lead to decisions in our favour, to predict competitor activity, to get the best out of the organisations we collaborate with, we need to know as much as we can about them.

Sources of information

There are many sources of information, some formal, some informal, some free and some very expensive. Our own business will be best served by a combination which we alone can select and mobilise. The kind of information we may need is discussed below. To provide a comprehensive list of information sources would fill a volume in itself, and even if it were possible here, covering the interests of our whole industry in a single list might not be the most helpful thing to do. E.M. Forster has been quoted as saying, 'Spoonfeeding in the long run teaches us nothing but the shape of the spoon'. Accordingly, the following notes suggest how to go about finding sources rather than citing the sources themselves.

Reference books

There is a prodigious supply of reference books. Any newcomer to the task of finding marketing information should spend some time in one or more of the main libraries that cater for business users. These include the principal public reference libraries in most cities and county towns. The City of London operates a library which specialises in business services: The City Business Library, 106 Fenchurch Street, London EC3. And of course there are the professional and academic libraries to which individuals may have access. Some of the more important reference books are not available in bookshops, but are distributed by the publishers by mail order. A few days browsing through the libraries, and perhaps undertaking a search for specific information, will show which books should be acquired for dedicated use in the office, and which are best left for reference in the library. The titles, publishers and means of acquisition are readily discovered from the volumes themselves.

For private sector UK industry and commerce, *Kompass* is the familiar and indispensable set of black tomes which graces the shelves of all business libraries and most marketing departments. *Who owns whom* lists parent companies and subsidiaries, giving access from either the name of the subsidiary or the parent. Local government is an important provider of work for the construction industry; in that sector *The municipal yearbook* is the vital source. Information and points of contact for central government are given in the *Civil service yearbook* published by Her Majesty's Stationery Office (HMSO) every March. Most nationalised industries publish a yearbook of some sort, as do many national professional bodies and trade associations. Key publishers include Kompass, Dun & Bradstreet, Extel, HMSO, The Economist, The Times and The Financial Times.

Directories are an expensive commodity: the books themselves are quite costly, and most are reissued and should be replaced at least every year. Through no fault of the publisher, the information they contain may not remain accurate even for their twelve months' nominal life. Indeed, because organisations change so frequently—they move office, the managers are promoted or retire, there are mergers and acquisitions, firms go out of business—many entries may be out of date before they are published. While establishing an information function, it is advisable not to order the initial set of reference books until we have a clear picture of the likely overall requirements. It is worth using the library for a few weeks before confirming a list that will suit our needs and our budget.

On-line data systems

The big users of on-line electronic data systems are financial institutions in the City. Big deals must be based on prodigious quantities of the best and most up-to-date information. Fast deals require relevant information to be instantly available. On-line systems are therefore very efficient and may be very expensive. Data is available in a range of areas, notably: financial information such as exchange and interest rates, securities and commodities prices; company information including summaries of recent annual reports and analysts' reports; principal press references and media information, i.e. an on-line all-media 'cuttings' facility, accessible by key words; and library and technical data. The company services and media services can be very valuable sources of marketing information. To attend a meeting having read a digest of the firm's last three annual reports and of twelve months' national and trade press cuttings places one in a strong position.

On-line services are quite expensive to access as well as to acquire: entry to some systems costs about the same amount per minute as an intercontinental peak time telephone call. Access should be limited to ensure that entry is purposeful, authorised and under proper control.

Official statistics and publications

Almost all official statistics and publications are issued through HMSO. A wide range of information is available about the construction industry and the sectors that it serves. HMSO has bookshops in High Holborn, London; Broad Street, Birmingham; Wine Street, Bristol; Princess Street, Manchester; Chichester Street, Belfast; and Lothian Road, Edinburgh. The main telephone number for general enquiries is 071-873 0011.

The press

One can gain a great deal of information simply by reading the papers. We must know what the regional, national and trade press is saying about us, and we can discover a lot about our markets, customers and competitors. The search for and handling of the resulting information must be tackled systematically. Depending on our needs, we may undertake the entire operation in-house, or we may contract all or part of it to one of the many commercial press-cutting services.

Contracting out is fairly straightforward for information about ourselves, for which a limited number of business names, product names, or other key search words may be used. Obtaining more general information on various aspects of the marketplace is less easy to place outside, and may be better undertaken by our own staff. The individual concerned must have a general awareness of the areas of interest and of the kind of information required. Photocopies of cuttings may be circulated, or a digest list prepared. The main daily and Sunday broadsheet newspapers and the leading construction industry technical journals should cover most needs. The *Economist* is of great value for up-to-date economic and political information which affects our markets. If we do business on a significant scale in a particular sector, it is worth monitoring that sector's technical press.

Our own business

By definition, an established business is in touch with many of its potential customers, competitors and others who serve them both. With many of them, we already have contractual relationships of some sort. It is easier to gather information about our subcontractors and joint venture partners than about customers and competitors. We should review the kind of information we obtain (or could abstract with little additional effort) from our normal course of business, and consider what marketing uses it may serve.

Networks

'I've danced with a man, who's danced with a girl, who's danced with the Prince of Wales.' Networking is becoming recognised as an important marketing technique. Since civilisation began, and before anyone thought of it as a 'technique', knowing someone who knows someone has been a means for those with 'connections' to use the system to their advantage. This is not necessarily corrupt, just a method of collecting information and introductions. We each belong to a number of networks. The network of friends and acquaintances can be mobilised to the mutual advantage of its members. We all went to school, and our contemporaries are now in many walks of life. This applies not only to Eton, Harrow and Winchester: the local comprehensive, particularly in a regional context, can be as valuable a connection. We belong to clubs: not necessarily clubs in St James's; perhaps a suburban tennis club. There are former colleagues. What about our neighbours? And people we meet on trains and aeroplanes and exchange business cards with? There is no conspiracy, it is just that we each know a large number of people, who in turn know others. What is it we need to know? Who is one stage closer to it than we are? Can we move a stage closer?

Company information

In addition to the information available from directories or on-line services, all the statutory returns made by limited companies are available for inspection at Companies House. There are search rooms in London and Cardiff (and Edinburgh for companies registered in Scotland) in which, for a small fee, any member of the public may obtain and read a microfiche containing a great deal of financial and other information on any limited company. Numerous firms based near the search rooms specialise in obtaining information for clients. The addresses are: Companies House, 55–71 City Road, London EC1; Companies House, Crown Way, Cardiff; and Companies House, 102 George Street, Edinburgh.

Commercial leads services

The construction industry is served by several organisations that assemble and publish, on a subscription basis, information on forthcoming projects. The source of the information is generally the publicly available papers from local authority planning committees, and other official sources such as the *EC Journal*. This information is of great value in what we may think of as the industry's internal market. But because the projects have been submitted for town planning approval or advertised officially for European tender action, they are well established and have reached at least the design stage. This means that the main design and management appointments are likely to have been made.

The ear to the ground

Information can come from amazing sources. If we predispose ourselves and our colleagues to recognising information that may be to our advantage, it is surprising how much turns up. In our daily working, domestic and leisure lives we are bombarded with information, most of which is of little value and almost all of which goes unnoticed. It is worth reviewing our information needs and offering a brief to as many individuals as possible.

And a little bit of lateral thinking

When we need specific information, we should not limit our thinking to conventional means of obtaining it. As in all areas of human endeavour, and more than ever in marketing, a little lateral thinking can give a disproportionate advantage.

Market information

It is necessary to distinguish between information about the market in general and about individual customers. As we have seen, in order to plan our marketing activity we must find out which sectors our potential customers are in, and discover enough about those potential customers in general to enable us to decide what to offer them and what arguments to use to persuade them. Only when we have set out our stall on the basis of this information do we become concerned about individual customers.

Market information falls into three broad areas. There are external economic, political and other factors which condition the whole sector. There are facts about the market itself, its current size, its potential growth or otherwise, its geographical distribution and the kind of customer organisations involved. And there is information about the needs and preferences of typical customer organisations.

Consider the consumer market example of a holiday firm which has positioned itself to serve a high added value, but still fairly high volume segment of the UK package holiday market—fly–drive to the USA. It must first consider the major economic factors. What is the present dollar/sterling exchange rate, how will it change and what does that mean for the market? Are the domestic economic factors that govern the outlook of the target group, who are likely to be professional and managerial couples with grown-up families, favourable to spending money on relatively expensive holidays? Then it must look at the market itself. How many people does the target group contain? How many of them take similar holidays? What share of that market does its target volume represent? Is demand growing? And then it needs to discover, probably by asking sample customers from the target group, what features of such holidays are likely to be attractive, where are the places of most interest, and what kind of package is best. This is information about the market in general; individual potential customers are consulted only on a sample basis for their representative views.

In our own industry, we might be considering a design–build package aimed at commercial property developers. We start by considering the economic conditions that affect property development: interest rates, current rental values and trends, business confidence of the potential occupiers of additional or better space, etc. We then look at the market itself. What is actually happening? Are developers considering new schemes? Looking at the projects they already have in hand, and the likely medium-term pattern of demand in the various development sectors we can serve, is what we can see happening consistent with our reading of the market? Which sectors are likely to be most active? Then, thinking of the product itself and customers' reaction to it, will developers respond to design–build? What are their needs? Can we shape our package to suit their need for firm schemes and prices at limited up-front cost, followed by performance and flexibility? If we are established in this sector, we should be able to find sources of the economic and market information fairly close to home. We probably know a number of target customers already. We can go and talk to some of them to discover whether or not the product we have in mind may be of interest, and what problems it would solve (or cause).

If we have the skill, we can undertake this 'market research' in-house. Alternatively, we may feel the need to employ an expert consultant: in this case, we must satisfy ourselves that the 'expert' is genuine! Does he have experience of the particular market? Are we being stampeded into a clipboard programme of interviews to obtain sample customer views before we are sure we know the economic and market factors, or even before we know what the product is?

Customer information

As we have seen, the main kind of marketing activity for the construction industry is the business-to-business marketing of services. In this area, not only must the customer be aware of us and of our product, but as we must take the initiative in building relationships with individual customers, we must start by knowing who and where the customer is. An essential component of marketing is therefore the collection of information on customers and potential customers.

We have reviewed the main sources of information. We must maintain a systematic live record of individual customer organisations: their addresses, premises and individuals with whom we have or may have contact. Each customer file should contain basic information about the organisation itself and a record of all significant transactions between ourselves and the customer. Which transactions we record must depend on the nature of our business and our marketing activity. In most cases there should be a note of sales letters and meetings, telephone approaches, enquiries received, offers submitted, contracts secured, and so on. This means that we have a picture of the developing or established relationship to which we can refer before any new approach or response is made. This kind of customer data file is particularly important if there are likely to be a number of different points of contact on both sides. There is nothing more embarrassing than, having said one's piece to an important potential customer, to be made aware that several colleagues have been in contact with the same individual on the same matter during the past few weeks!

Some individuals with sales responsibility find it difficult to share details of their contacts with their colleagues. They must be persuaded that registering a customer contact is an important prima facie signal of their 'ownership' of that contact.

Typical headings for a customer information database are suggested at the end of this chapter. Each marketing organisation will have particular needs, according to its internal structure and the nature of its customers. These suggestions should therefore be taken as a starting point rather than a model.

Competitor information

The last people we want to tell what we are doing are our competitors. This means that competitor information is probably the most difficult to come by. What do we need to know about our competitors? First we need to know who they are. Then we must try to understand their strategy for each segment of our market in which they are competing with us. Knowing about competitors is second in importance only to knowing about customers.

In addition to the common sources of information about any company, there are two obvious means of obtaining competitor information. The first is to watch them carefully as they compete with us, and to record and interpret as much as possible to help us understand their strategy. The second is to take stock of all the other relationships we may have with a competitor organisation—through trade associations, subcontracts and joint ventures, staff transferring from them to us—and use these relationships, without of course betraying any mutual trust, to discover more about the competitor's activities, strengths and weaknesses.

Watching the performance of a competitor when actually preparing and submitting a competitive bid is, of course, only a small part of what is required. We must piece together as much evidence as we can of the competitor's whole marketing effort. We should consider our own overall competitive strategy and recognise that a serious competitor will be engaged in the same kind of activities. Having thus identified the kind of things competitors may be doing, we can look closely for signs of them. But our observation of competitors should not only be defensive: the best ones are certain to be adopting strategies we have not thought of. We can learn positive lessons as well as preparing for defence.

We must maintain a set of competitor files similar to those we keep for customers. Each will contain 'header' information about the organisation itself and 'transactional' information about specific events. If other parts of our own organisation are engaged in a range of activities, we will come across competing firms in many different relationships. Subject to the need for Chinese walls, the opportunity to share the information thus available creates considerable advantage. Some notes on establishing a competitor information database are given at the end of this chapter.

Pricing information

In most sectors of the construction industry, we calculate our prices on the basis of our estimated costs and overheads and the margin for profit we believe will not make us uncompetitive. This is cost-related pricing. In many other industries, the first input to the pricing process is what the product could be sold for in the market. We are so used to competitive tendering that we forget that price can be an important marketing tool in other ways.

The manager of a small gentlemen's outfitting shop in the Midlands used to say that during the lean times of the early 1930s he had a stock of half-guinea caps. For what would now be $52\frac{1}{2}$p, these were quite good quality men's caps. They did not sell at full price, nor was he able to move them in his sale at seven shillings and sixpence. After the sale, however, he gave them pride of place in the shop window at the price of a full guinea, and sold the lot within a week. Remember the four Ps of the marketing mix—product, promotion, price and place. The product was the same; the caps were sold by pride of place and the promotion of offering them at a price which suggested that they were something out of the ordinary. We must remember that there is not only a competitive price, but also an optimum market price.

It is important that we know as much as possible about competitor pricing: we may then review prices which have been prepared on a cost basis to make sure that we are neither losing price opportunity nor offering our product to the market at a price it will not respect. This question is of special importance in providing advisory services. A lifetime of experience may lead to one hour of discussion with a client which saves the client a million pounds. How do we price that hour?

Information to manage the sales and bidding process

The lifeblood of our business is the inflow of new orders. It is therefore of paramount importance that we manage enquiries with the greatest possible efficiency. The right decisions must be taken at the right time. Resources must be allocated and priorities set. For this type of management, the best possible information is required.

Enquiries pass through distinct phases in their transition from initial discussions to an eventual order to proceed with the work. Each phase needs a different kind of attention, and the volume of potential business in each phase at any time provides a measure of both our sales and marketing performance and our organisation's likely future inflow of new business. The arrangement of information in what we sometimes describe as an 'enquiry tracking system' should recognise these phases. Enquiries can be categorised as follows.

- *Potential enquiry:* we have identified a specific item of business about which we are in discussion with the client and for which we expect an opportunity to make a firm proposal.
- *Active enquiry:* we are preparing firm proposals or prices which will be submitted to a client for active consideration.
- *Potential contract:* the client has signified that he intends to proceed with the work and to place the order with us.
- *Order received:* that intention has been translated into some form of binding contract.

The tracking system should contain four sections, one for each of these phases. Enquiries progress from one section to the next as we move nearer to receiving the order, or they may disappear as we lose them to a competitor or other hazard.

An enquiry should be allocated a reference number at the point at which it is identified as a specific item of possible future business. The act of allocating a number may have particular significance in some companies, for example where incentives are awarded to sales staff for bringing in enquiries. The number may be a simple serial, but where we need to register different types of work or work handled by different departments or disciplines, a system of numbers is required which indicates those differences.

The end product of our enquiry tracking information system is a periodic report which can be used by the appropriate manager to review progress on all enquiries or those for which he is responsible and to take any necessary decisions on them. The report should include the client's name, enquiry title, estimated value (capital value or fees value as appropriate), date for proposal or bid submission, internal programme dates for completion of technical information, estimate, board approval of prices, and any brief notes necessary to record the status of the enquiry or any decisions taken about it. The usual procedure is for the manager to hold a periodic (perhaps weekly) meeting with the functional heads responsible for proposal writing, design, estimating, planning and discussions with clients, using the report as an agenda and using the transactions of the meeting to amend the report for the next time.

The fourth section of the enquiry tracking information system is very important. It is all too easy for our organisation to relax as soon as the client has indicated that he has decided, subject to reaching final agreement, to place the order with us. There may then be a gap between the forces in our organisation directed towards obtaining work and those that are to execute it. The information and other systems that manage the sales and marketing process must follow right through to the signing of a contract, and then formally hand over a well-documented commitment to the colleagues who will have to deliver the goods. Some further notes on enquiry tracking systems are given at the end of this chapter.

Information handling

In the early 1990s, when a complete desktop computer system for database, spreadsheet and word processing can be obtained for well under £1000, no business need be without some form of modern electronic information technology. But everyone, from a sole trader to a mighty corporation, must remember that the data handling systems are our slaves rather than our masters.

In the spirit of Mies van der Rohe, who convinced architects and designers of his generation that 'less is more', and of the person who apologised for a long letter, not having had time to write a short one, we must make sure that our computer systems do what is required of them simply and effectively but do not introduce unnecessary complications.

A generation ago, our customer information and competitor information would have been held in a master card index system, laboriously kept up to date by a roomful of clerical staff. The day-to-day management of enquiries would probably have been controlled by a typewritten (remember the Roneo duplicator?) set of minutes, retyped no less laboriously after each weekly 'enquiry meeting'. In the 1990s the customer and competitor information is invariably held in some form of database system; for small organisations on a free-standing desktop computer, for larger organisations on a central system. The weekly report is at least held on a word processor and easily updated, at best produced from the database drawing on static data about the client and transactional data about the enquiries themselves from separate files.

The purpose of the information system is to support marketing and sales activities and to manage the handling of enquiries. It is not to entertain computer buffs in the organisation or in its consultants. Less is therefore very much more! Few organisations need to create anything bigger than a competent desktop computer-based system.

Customer information

1. Information about the potential customer organisation. This section contains fixed details of the target organisation. It should be reviewed on a regular basis and updated when changes become known.

Name:
Telephone: Address: Fax: Telex:

Parent Company:

Relevant Associate Companies:

Nature of business:

Notes on corporate policy, organisation structure, and any other factors which may have a bearing on the potential customer's approach to the purchase of our products:

Our Interest: (e.g. for which products, departments, subsidiaries, etc.).

2. Information on contact individuals. This section contains personal details of all contacts and other known decision-makers, gate-keepers or other individuals who may be involved in providing access to the organisation or in decisions about the purchase of our product.

Name: Job title:
Location: Direct line telephone: Direct fax:
Address:

Job function: (particularly in relation to our purchasing decisions).

Personal information: (The nature of information here will vary—it should build up a profile of the individual to assist in developing personal and corporate relationships. Information should include product preferences and attitudes, relationship with competitors, technical/career background, management style, level of delegation, etc. Personal interests and tastes, e.g. golf, racing, music, opera, shooting, sailing, etc.—if we hold a golf day, have a box at the opera or seats at Wimbledon, our database should be able to tell us who is likely to be interested. Personal details such as home address, spouse's name, children, school or university, etc.)

3. Transactional information: This section records all significant 'transactions' with the potential customer organisation. The manner and the amount of detail must depend on our business. Personal approaches, meetings, mailshots, key sales correspondence, information obtained formally or informally about potential business, etc. Where a specific enquiry or contract is obtained, there should be

Competitor information

1. Information about the competitor organisation. This section contains fixed details of the known competitor. It should be reviewed on a regular basis and updated when changes become known.

   Name:

   Telephone: Address:

                                             Fax: Telex:

   Parent Company:

   Relevant Associate Companies:

   Area of competition:

   Notes on corporate policy, organisation structure, marketing strategy, sales and competitive tactics which may be of value in shaping our competitive response:

   Our Interest: (e.g. for which products, departments, subsidiaries, etc.).

2. Information on contact individuals. This section contains information about individuals who may be approached where contact is required, e.g. to discuss joint ventures etc.

   Name: Job title:

   Location: Direct line telephone: Direct fax:

   Address:

   Job function:

   Relationship with: (our own people)

   Name: Nature of relationship:

3. Transactional information: This section records all significant 'transactions' with the potential competitor organisation. The manner and the amount of detail must depend on our business. Most 'transactions' will relate to our experience of its performance as a competitor—interest expressed in new business, strong client relationships, prices submitted, etc. but other information should include press reports, marketplace gossip, a note of other corporate relationships, e.g. joint ventures etc.

67

Enquiry tracking

The focus of the enquiry tracking system is the regular (weekly or at another suitable interval) scheduling the current status, progress, decisions, planned future action, submission and other dates, etc. for all current enquiries. As the handling of enquiries requires different approaches at different stages of their gestation, the report should be divided by stages as suggested above, i.e. potential enquiries, active enquiries, potential contracts, orders received.

Possible report formats are suggested below. Individual needs will vary. The means of holding underlying data is a matter of need and available systems. For a relatively small business, the report could be held as a simple word processor document which is updated regularly from notes made on the hard copy at the regular enquiry review meeting.

A separate entry is required for each project under its appropriate section as shown. System permitting, separate reports can be prepared for each project manager, functional department etc.

1. Potential enquiries

Customer: Project title:

Name of primary contact: Estimated value:

Brief note on project scope: Our manager responsible for pursuit:

Date active enquiry expected: Possible programme dates:

Action required now:

2. Active enquiries

Enquiry number: Project title:

Estimated value:

Name of primary contact: Customer:

Brief note on enquiry scope: Enquiry project manager:

Programme: *Event:*   *Date:*   *Comment:*

              Receive enquiry
              Briefing meeting
              Design
              Estimate
              Price review

3. Potential contracts

   Report layout similar to active enquiries, but programme and action headings appropriate to the stage where we believe the competition has been eliminated, and the customer has decided to go ahead—with us.

4. Orders received

   As above, but now, after a formal decision from the customer, monitoring the final steps of ensuring that contracts are signed, documentation is confirmed and responsibility is handed over for implementation.

69

5. Getting the enquiry

First we should define the term 'enquiry', which is sometimes misunderstood. An enquiry is a specific piece of business which has been identified for active pursuit. It remains an enquiry until it is lost, abandoned or converted into a contract. The more general sense of the word suggests to some people that it should only signify an approach from a client who 'enquires' if we would like to do some work for him. This is not so, but it is presumably the origin of the term as used in a marketing context. Some guidelines on classifying, recording and reporting on enquiries are given in chapter 4.

When do general discussions about business turn into a formal enquiry? This is a matter for debate in many organisations. Most management accounting systems require the allocation of a job number for any item of work on which costs are to be expended. In most cases, therefore, an enquiry should be recognised and a number allocated to it when we take a decision to prepare a formal proposal or to undertake specific design or estimating work. Precise arrangements depend on the internal administration of the firm. In cases where sales staff are rewarded for bringing in enquiries, this is clearly a sensitive and important matter.

The strategy for sales

Chapter 1 outlined the processes of business-to-business marketing, with particular reference to the construction industry. We saw the need to build relationships as the main means of obtaining new work. Chapter 2 showed how analysis of our potential markets leads to a definition of what products we intend to offer to what kind of customers. This chapter aims to show how the strategy and the information can be brought together to secure enquiries from our target customers.

Sector research—the target list

In chapter 4 we recognised the many sources of information that can be used to identify potential customer organisations and individual points of contact within them. By one of the means outlined, we must prepare an initial target list for each segment of our market.

Decision-makers and their friends

Corporate decision making is a subject of study in its own right. We are interested in the 'decision to buy', which is the ultimate objective of all our marketing activity. To help us to understand how a company makes a decision to buy, let us think about the domestic chore of buying a packet of cornflakes. This introduces the concept known in marketing as the decision making unit (DMU). The DMU is a group of people each of whom contributes in some way to the decision.

On the face of it, a decision to buy a packet of breakfast cereal is taken at the supermarket shelf. The buyer enters the store, looks at the array of cereals on the shelf, makes a choice and takes the chosen pack to the checkout with the rest of a trolley-full of goods. But is the decision taken there? The final decision may well be, but the shopper's decision is influenced by two other important factors. One is the preferences of other members of the family. The younger ones have clear views and express them strongly. They are 'influencers' of the decision to buy. In some families, mother may save her weekly shopping expedition for Saturday, when father is free to drive her to the superstore and help to carry the goods. She wants to go to the new store on the bypass. He remembers last week when the traffic jam on the main road blocked the shoppers' car park and the family sat in the car for an hour, unable to get into the store or out onto the road. He insists on shopping elsewhere. Father did not influence the decision to buy, but he was a 'gatekeeper', denying access to that superstore.

The family is a decision-making unit. Each member may influence the decision or have power over whether or not the transaction is possible. The manufacturer of the breakfast cereal product and the owner of the superstore must consider the whole family decision-making unit. The cereal manufacturer directs his advertising at mother and children. The messages to them may be quite different. Mother wants to feel that she is a good mother; she wants the children to grow up to be brainy, healthy and so on. The children will respond to advertisements designed to appeal to them. The superstore owner must locate and design the store so that it attracts those members of the family who have a say in where the family does its shopping.

Business decisions to buy are taken by decision-making units in the same sort of way. The decision-maker may be a senior individual, a board or a committee. There will be others whose advice is taken or who otherwise influence the decision. And there are 'gatekeepers' who can stop or delay the transaction. In each organisation we deal with, we must try to understand the decision-making process and the part played by the various members of the particular decision-making unit, any one of whom we neglect at our peril. And we must remember that things are not always as they appear at first sight. The nominal decision-maker may be referring back to the real decision-maker, who is hidden somewhere in the depths of the organisation.

Consider, for example, the appointment of an architect by the local branch of a big multinational company. The local project manager invites proposals and gives no hint that he has to seek approval elsewhere. He has appointed a firm of chartered surveyors to advise on town planning, funding, development value and so on. In seeking the commission we succeed in getting quite close to the project manager; he is our potential client and he seems to favour us. One of our partners is working on another project with the chartered surveyor. We keep him in the picture and make sure that when his advice is sought by the project manager, any answer about our firm is very positive. We submit our proposals. When we telephone the project manager to see how things are going, we get the impression from his secretary that he is out of the office a great deal. Eventually we learn that an American architect has been appointed.

We failed to identify two essential components of the decision-making unit. First of all, the secretary is a gatekeeper. We treated her in an offhand manner on the telephone and ignored her when we attended meetings at the project manager's office. She, quite understandably therefore, was not on our side, and denied us access to the project manager at the critical time when he could have told us that he was having to consult the group chief architect at headquarters in Chicago. But we should have discovered for ourselves the existence of the group chief architect and the extent of his influence at a much earlier date.

From our very first approach, we must recognise that the corporate decision to buy may be a very complex one, taken within a matrix of decision-makers and influencers, to whom access is gained through other individuals who act as gatekeepers. As we get to know more about the potential client, progressing from information assembly through early discussions to the eventual handling of a firm enquiry, we must piece together the decision-making matrix and make sure that we recognise the decision-making unit and take it into account. And we must remember that the members of this decision-making matrix are colleagues in one organisation. They have a complex internal relationship of friends and non-friends, allies and rivals, communication and non-communication. It is not just a question of making sure that the key people are on our side. We must be sensitive to the politcal dimension. It may be over Mr A's dead body that anyone favoured by Mr B will get business from the organisation. And in pursuing our interests within the client team, we must not be seen to be so active in lobbying everyone in sight that we get up the nose of the whole team, friend and foe alike!

In a typical large organisation which buys building and property services on a regular basis, the 'decision to buy' team may include, as decision-makers or influencers: the line manager (project manager, engineering manager, property manager, development manager, and so on) who has direct responsibility for the work, and his subordinates; a director, general manager or board to whom he reports; internal specialists such as engineers, architects, quantity surveyors, accountants and the like, who are not under the direct control of the line manager; external consultants of various disciplines; and for a subsidiary or branch organisation, this whole structure replicated at head office. Such an organisation keeps a list of approved firms for each type of work. The people who control this list are strategic gatekeepers. Without their agreement we do not get to the starting gate. Then there are the tactical gatekeepers who control day-to-day contact with the client's team by managing access to them. These include the telephonists, receptionists and secretaries.

The decision-maker has a lot of friends, and they must be our friends too.

Securing a meeting

No single approach is guaranteed to secure a meeting with an unknown target decision-maker. The three main opening options are

- to write a letter
- to telephone
- to gain an introduction through an intermediary.

Each of us has a different balance of skills and different preferences. If one of our personal strengths is that we have a very wide range of personal contacts, the intermediary route may be the best. An individual with a confident persuasive telephone manner, skilled in making 'cold' telephone approaches may do best with that approach. Others may find that placing a compelling single page of text on the client's desk before telephoning does the trick.

In certain circumstances, the intermediary route is a powerful one. It involves the network mentioned in chapter 4, extended beyond the mere collection of information. A little constructive thought can get direct personal introductions in many target organisations. The limitation of the network approach in arranging actual meetings is one of motivation. Our acquaintance has his own job to do and his own reputation to guard. These will generally take priority.

Cold telephoning is an option which works well for some people and in some situations. Getting the secretary on one's side requires a great deal of confidence, a lot of charm and, above all, a product in which the target is likely to take an interest. If our marketing strategy is right, a high proportion of our approaches will be made to potentially willing customers. Executive search consultants, so-called headhunters, make their living by cold-calling senior people on the telephone. Perhaps that underlines what we say about confidence, charm and above all, the product. Who is not curious to hear what the headhunter has to offer when he comes on the line?

The most generally reliable route to a first meeting with a target customer is the personal letter with a telephone follow-up. This is not to be confused with 'direct mail' in which standard letters are posted in large numbers and we await the potential customer's response. The average response to such letters, even with a well selected list, is said to be between 2% and 3%. It therefore works only where we have a very long list of targets and expect to do business with a very small proportion of them.

We are trying to build a relationship. To start that process we need to get a first meeting. This is the single purpose of our approach, and our letter should be very carefully drafted with this object in mind. We come back to the old rule that we must 'place ourselves in the position of the customer'. We must try to understand his position. Consider his aims and problems. Anticipate potential objections. See the whole transaction from his point of view. In shaping our argument, we must consider carefully what the customer knows and does not know about us. We may otherwise highlight weaknesses of which he was not aware, by trying to explain them away. The letter must be personal. It must be short. It must be positive. And it must be directed solely at obtaining a meeting.

Individuals develop their own styles for these letters. One of the most effective has three simple paragraphs. The first is about the customer and his situation; it captures his attention. The second is about the product and its benefits for the customer; it must make him an offer he cannot refuse. The third says what we are going to do to take the customer a step closer to having those benefits; it leaves us with the initiative.

We should spend time drafting model letters for each type of approach, to avoid inventing the wheel every time. But we must look very carefully at the model letter with each target customer in mind. This applies particularly to the first paragraph. The example shown in Fig. 1 is for an approach by a planned-maintenance contractor to a national institution with central premises and high-street shops.

The letter is addressed personally and signed personally—never, ever, 'p.p.' by a secretary. The first paragraph is what catches the addressee's eye. It must say something about his organisation or about him as an

Dear Mr Bloggs

The maintenance of Bloggs plc's head office complex in Wigan, your five regional distribution centres and your 300 high-street branches must represent a very significant overhead cost.

Whizzo Planned Maintenance provides a nationwide service through a network of over a hundred local depots. Skilful planning and management, national buying power and the use of local resources result in a uniquely cost-effective service. We have demonstrated to our clients that we can achieve significant savings in cost, and often improvements in standards at the same time.

I would welcome an opportunity of giving you some further information on what can be achieved. I will, if I may, telephone you during the early part of next week to see whether we can make an appointment for a brief meeting.

Yours sincerely

John Writer
Whizzo Planned Maintenance

Fig. 1. Sample model letter

individual that immediately makes it clear that it is not a standard letter, but one which was written with him in mind. Mere inclusion of the individual's name or the name of his company in an otherwise standard opening sentence is an awkward ploy which, in these days of word processors, will be recognised as such. If there is a relevant common acquaintance, mention it. If Mr Bloggs' name came from a conference list, consider, 'I believe we met briefly at ...' Resist the temptation to send a brochure at this stage. Save that for the meeting. Inclusion of a brochure devalues the letter and makes it much less likely to be read. It also invites the 'Thank you for sending me a brochure outlining your firm's services, I will keep it on the file against possible future need' response, which virtually closes the door to further contact.

The pace of sending out such letters must be governed by the pace at which the signatory can follow them up and obtain a face-to-face meeting with a proportion of them. Whether that pace is five, ten or twenty letters a week will be discovered by experience. It depends on the rate of response and the availability of the writer.

The writer should follow up the letters personally, rather than delegating the task to a secretary or assistant. Delegating the follow-up call can appear either self-important or casual. There is no reason for a secretary not to initiate the call. 'Is Mr Bloggs available for a brief word with Mr Writer of Whizzo Planned Maintenance, please?' 'What is it about?' 'Mr Writer wrote to Mr Bloggs last week suggesting that they should meet.' The 'suggesting they should meet' line implies a relationship of peers. The alternative of 'asking whether you would see him to discuss whether you were interested in buying our services' reduces Mr Writer to door-knocking salesman status. And at this point, in any case, all he is selling is the idea of a meeting. The secretary offering the manager on the line is an approach which may succeed because it signals the status of the caller. Bloggs' secretary may ask for Writer to be put on the line. He should be ready and waiting to speak to either Bloggs or his secretary. The secretary may offer to make an appointment 'without disturbing Mr Bloggs'. If Bloggs' secretary stonewalls, one way forward for Writer's secretary is the 'Shall we pencil in something for them both to confirm?' approach. If it becomes clear that Bloggs is not amenable to such an approach, the fall-back may be to ask whether there is someone else in Mr Bloggs' organisation with whom it may be appropriate for Mr Writer to get in touch. This opens the way for the next approach to be made on a 'Mr Bloggs asked me to call you' basis, but do not get caught out pretending that there is a relationship with Bloggs when there is not!

Telephone selling experts write scripts for this sort of exercise, which are worth trying. The script gives the caller options which depend on the response to the previous question or request, and can be refined with experience of the first few calls.

We must develop our own techniques. These calls must have the aura of a senior manager approaching his peer with an offer to do business to the advantage of both parties. If it is too slick and obviously scripted, that aura will be destroyed. We are selling. We need to be natural, unflustered, unpressuring, unthreatening and, above all, to sound as though we would be very pleasant to deal with.

It may take several calls to secure a meeting. We should not pursue the matter to the point of irritation. Read the signals and quit while we're ahead. But always retain the initiative. We all know what 'Don't call us, we'll call you' means!

The initial meeting

The initial meeting is very important. It may well be a one-shot opportunity. It is worth putting in a good deal of effort to prepare for it.

Take another look at the information you have already obtained on the potential client organisation. Is there anything you do not know that would be useful for the first discussion? Look up the individual. In particular, look for factors you have in common. If he is senior, particularly in the public sector, he will have an entry in *Who's Who*. Most professions and trade associations have directories of their senior personalities. In many towns and cities the local newspaper publishes an annual reference book of the great and the good. One golden rule though—never mention the fact that you have looked up the client in the directory. One of the worst things you can say is 'I was looking at your entry in *Who's Who* this morning...' It is almost always an embarrassing conversation stopper. Personal information and company information should be used in the background. Never tell the client about his own company. He knows a lot more about it than you do. But use the information to lead the discussion in the direction you want it to go. Ask questions in the light of your research to draw out confirming answers. You should appear to be quietly knowledgeable about the individual and the firm. We are all flattered by a visitor who seems, as a matter of course, to know about us and our firm. It makes us feel important.

Lay down an objective for the meeting. The objective should be attainable. It should take you firmly in the direction you want to go. If you are discussing a specific work opportunity, you should decide how to approach it and what you expect this meeting to achieve. Do you want to be put on a bid list? Do you want to discover who is making the bid list? Are you trying to deflect the client into a negotiated deal? In the absence of any specific business opportunity, the aim of the meeting is to establish a personal rapport, to discover as much as possible about the plans of the potential client company, and to make quite sure that you leave the meeting with the further development of the relationship under your own control.

Decide who should attend the meeting. In general, two representatives are better than one, if the size and value of potential business justifies it. One person can observe the discussion from one side while the other is enmeshed in the debate. Avoid going 'mob-handed'. But if there is the least measure of confidentiality, security or conspiracy to be expected of the meeting, one person on his own, keeping his pen in his pocket, is the order of the day. The client will say things to one person that he would not dream of saying to two, particularly if nothing is written down.

This opening meeting, whether with a decision-maker or an intermediary, can be considered in three phases.

Phase 1: social

Start by breaking the ice and beginning to establish the common ground that is the substance of a business friendship. Avoid getting down to serious business for the present. Find social, domestic or professional matters, acquaintances in common, hobbies, other interests, places, old school, and so on. With a little practice, it is possible quite naturally to discover areas of mutual interest. Let the conversation flow naturally and sense the client's mood. At the first sign of impatience with the social niceties, shift the emphasis to general business or professional matters, or move straight on to phase 2. An old-fashioned salesman would keep a loose-leaf book (today it would be a Filofax or a pocket computer) in which he recorded, after leaving the premises, personal information, views and opinions gleaned during such a discussion. This would be carefully stored and retrieved for the next meeting. Taking an interest in someone with whom we do business is perfectly natural. We are all impressed with people who remember our spouse's name or that we are interested in bird-watching. But to discover that it is all done with the aid of a computer database is a different matter.

Phase 2: business

At an appropriate moment, steer the conversation towards the matter you have decided you need to discuss at this particular meeting. The initial meeting should discover or confirm the policies, problems, organisation and plans of the client. It should establish, if we have not done so already, whether there is likely to be any interest in the kind of service we provide. Are there any suitable projects or other proposals in the pipeline? How can we best move forward towards obtaining business?

We must not confine ourselves to asking for opportunities to tender for work the client has already decided upon. We must think creatively and make suggestions or offer stratagems that anticipate the client's needs and give us an inside track to fulfil them. Once again, this is only possible if we 'place ourselves in the position of the customer', and understand his problems and his motivation—understand what is in it for him. The marketing buzz-word for this is 'benefit selling', but it is more than selling benefits. It is a state of mind which enables us to see our opponent's cards. A manager is motivated by business advantage. The sure way to move forward is to offer something that may get him more business, improve his service to his own customer, reduce the cost of his product, reduce his overheads, etc.—any of the things we would like to achieve ourselves.

Phase 3: the link to the future

Provided that nothing has happened during the meeting to make us decide that the organisation is not a potential client, we must make sure that we close with some good reason for further interaction—with the initiative in our hands. If we lose the initiative, the client may let matters ride and we shall find it very difficult to reopen the door.

Finally, a golden rule. As we leave the meeting, we must never, ever, discuss the meeting or the client's business until we are well clear of the building. Walls have ears!

Building the personal and corporate relationship

Two things must be recognised about a client who decides to place an order with us. First, his own performance will be judged by ours. Second, he will have to work with us. In this situation we all tend to favour someone we know and trust. Building real personal relationships is therefore central to getting new business. Beyond affecting decisions themselves, personal relationships provide advance information, an insight into the real needs of the client organisation and, within the limits of what may be proper, something of an inside track.

Great care must be taken not to allow such relationships to cross the all-important boundary between the legitimate and the improper. This boundary differs according to circumstances, and there is, of course, a measure of individual choice. It is worth remembering that different clients are governed by different ethical codes. For a public sector client, this has a great deal to do with accountability for public funds and even-handedness to suppliers and contractors. Public sector competitive tendering has as much to do with competition being seen to be 'fair' as with obtaining the lowest price. A private sector client has other criteria, more directed towards getting the best service, lowest price, best value for money, or competitive advantage to his own firm. The latter finds it easier to negotiate, strike a private bargain or accept a non-conforming bid. Hospitality is an important part of the relationship-building process. But we must take stock, and recognise clearly what we are doing, if we ever reach the point where either party begins to think of it as an inducement.

Creating the opportunity

The most important order we obtain from any client is the first one. As our relationship develops, unless we can see a significant order in the immediate pipeline, we should look for a relationship-cementing minor opportunity to do business together. It may be a small project; a study, a survey. Some care must be taken that this piece of business is one that will bring us closer to the client. If we are seeking major projects and the skills we are offering are specifically those appropriate to such projects, taking a small one may prove nothing. On the contrary, a small project may even be handled by different people in the client organisation and, by becoming their supplier, we may in fact undermine the very relationship we have painstakingly been building up. And the small job must not get lost between the cracks in our own organisation. If we do it at all, we must do it well. Many professional clients like to see how their contractors, consultants or suppliers perform with a small order before they entrust them with a big one. It may be a test. And the excuse that we are not geared up for a small job will not work. If that is so, we should not have taken it on!

Improving the odds by choosing the battle ground or getting first under the wire

If we reach the client at a sufficiently early stage in his development of the project, we may be able to influence the way in which it is handled, to our advantage. We believe that this will also be to the client's advantage because we are confident that we shall provide a better service than any of our competitors. If we do not have this confidence, we must look to the service we provide and improve it until we have. Techniques for improving the odds of securing the contract are dealt with in chapter 6. But in seeking the enquiry we should be aiming to get in early and to have a measure of influence over its handling.

Antennae, referrals, sources and cross-selling

What has been described is a systematic, painstaking way of establishing relationships in the organisations we have identified as potential clients and of using those relationships to obtain enquiries. That is our bread and butter route. But it is not, by any means, the only way.

As Doolittle says in 'My Fair Lady' on the night before his wedding day, 'There's drinks and girls all over London!'. So are there opportunities for business all around us if we set our antennae to recognise them. Our marketing strategy and our systematic search for relationships that produce enquiries are, as we have seen, a means of ensuring that our costly efforts to generate work are directed where they are most likely to succeed. But while adopting this positive systematic approach, we must be alive to the many opportunities that may arise from other sources.

In chapter 4 we considered the sources of external information that can lead to specific opportunities. Diligent reading of key national and regional newspapers and trade periodicals is one essential chore. We must, however, bear in mind that the most energetic of our competitors will have the same information, so we must tackle the task efficiently and quickly in order to stay one jump ahead. Commercial sources of 'leads' should be considered in the light of our specific needs. Their most significant sources of information are town planning applications and European

Community publication of public sector projects. They are therefore more appropriate to the contracting, subcontracting and materials sectors of the industry than to those offering design, project management or construction management services, for whom publication in that way comes at a later stage in the project than that at which they would prefer to become involved. And leads services are, by nature, likely to produce a relatively high proportion of price-competitive opportunities.

We work in a complex industry where teams of professionals, contractors, subcontractors and manufacturers form and dissolve for each project. Over a period of years we create a body of friends and contacts with whom we find it comfortable to do business. Each of us is in a different position, generally seeking different involvement in the same projects. By a system of referrals between friendly companies, we can multiply our search for new business by the number of organisations in the informal 'team'. This is a very powerful traditional source of business for the construction industry and its professions. Indeed, there are many firms whose business comes largely in this manner.

A large group with a number of subsidiaries in different sectors of the construction industry can gain significant advantage from internal referrals between subsidiaries. Using the contacts of one part of the organisation to obtain external business for another is called 'cross-selling'. Internally, main contractor subsidiaries can place business with subcontractor sister companies. By placing market-price subcontracts inside the group rather than outside, the group may almost double its turnover from having the main contract for a given project. But there are pitfalls. How does the main contractor know it is getting market prices? If it puts the subcontractors in competition with outside firms and then fails to place an order with the lowest tenderer, there will be problems in getting outside tenders when they are needed in the future. Some groups adopt the policy that at times when work is hard to come by, the main contractors must negotiate in-house subcontracts wherever they can, whereas at times when the subcontractor subsidiaries can fill their order books with profitable outside work, the main contractor subsidiaries scour the outside market for the most favourable subcontract prices. But come what may, a big group has an important selling network which it ignores to its disadvantage.

Day-to-day checks and balances

By means of routine checks and balances, we must know where our business is coming from. About eighty per cent of our new business opportunities will probably result from twenty per cent of our marketing effort. We cannot predict which twenty per cent this will be, but we can record it and try to learn to optimise our return for effort and expenditure. The marketplace changes. We must recognise the signals which indicate that change is on the way. And we must anticipate the changes, adjusting our activity before our competitors adjust theirs. Bonanzas and gravy trains come to and end; so do recessions. We must not assume that today is forever. And our daily checks and balances will tell us when a more thorough reappraisal is due. But that is a matter to be considered when the marketing audit is discussed in chapter 11.

6. Getting the contract

We have decided that an item of business is one we intend to obtain. We must set out our stall to get it. No messing: we are professionals and we shall, systematically and professionally, set about the process of making quite sure that we obtain an order. We first take stock of the situation. What stage has the work reached? Who else is aware of it, and how will their efforts to obtain it affect ours? What does the client really need? How can we make sure that we gain the initiative? Can we get an 'inside track'? And whether or not we face competitive tendering, we live in a world in which the natural laws of economics are rarely suspended: can we gain any pricing advantage?

Strategy for bidding with or without competition

There is, as seen in chapter 3, a very simple hierarchy of competitive strategy for a situation in which our competitive aim is to secure an order. Our priorities are as follows.

(1) Avoid competition by ensuring that competitors are not even aware of the opportunity.

(2) If there is competition, try to arrange for it to take place on our favoured ground.

(3) If price competition is inevitable, use all available tactics to submit the offer that will be accepted, by submitting the lowest price or otherwise.

The marketing reason for trying to avoid the direct price competition involved in competitive tendering is not that we can obtain a more profitable price by other means. It is to reduce the speculative costs we incur before being assured of an order. And, even more important, it is to increase the likelihood of obtaining the business.

Avoiding competition

We live in a competitive world. It is neither possible nor in the long term necessarily desirable to avoid competition. The competitors exist. They are as active as we are in the marketplace. It is a fact of economic life that in almost all markets, the spur of competitive activity, by improving the quality and value for money offered to the customer, increases the total volume of business available to the competitors as a group. All but the weakest competitors gain. By its nature, competition is a matter of the survival of the fittest. And if we did not intend to be among the fittest we would certainly not be taking an interest in marketing!

In the contracting world, however, there is a tendency to think that 'competition' and 'competitive tendering' are one and the same thing. So generally when we talk of avoiding competition, we mean avoiding the lottery of competitive tendering in which only one of our client-benefiting skills is brought to bear, that of being able to offer (not necessarily deliver) the lowest price for a fixed scope of work.

If we wait for work to come to us, competitive tendering is likely to be our lot. Not that there is anything wrong with tendering for work: a large volume of contracting and subcontracting work, and even some kinds of professional work, are available only by that route. To ignore it may deprive us of an important component of our profitable business mix. In our corporate strategy and hence in our marketing strategy, we must consider our commercial experience of all kinds of work. Of the types of work potentially available to us, some will earn a higher margin than others. Some will be available in greater volume. Some will involve speculative cost. Some will take time and effort to track down from an early stage. We need a mix of routine work, involving limited acquisition effort or cost and moderate margin, and other work which may take more effort to obtain but will provide a higher margin.

We can think of the market as a funnel down which the work opportunities flow. If we sit at the neck of the funnel where everybody else knows there is a steady flow of work, i.e. at the tender list stage, we face intense competition. If we venture up the funnel to meet the opportunities, to a point where we have to use a great deal of skill and experience to find them in a rarefied space, we will meet less direct competition and will be better placed to influence the terms on which the work is placed. In other words, we must set out to intercept new projects or other opportunities at an early stage in their development. We can do this in two ways: by offering products designed to meet clients' needs at an early stage in the project's life, and by taking those products with us to find the client before he has reached the point at which he is able to come and find us—and, of course, find all the others.

Almost all established construction industry disciplines can find products that lead them to the ultimate customer at the very inception of the project. All disciplines, without exception, can find products that lead them to their immediate customer within the contracting hierarchy at the inception of that customer's need for the particular specialist service.

The architect, quite naturally, offers brief taking and inception study services and, for a new building, is likely to be the client's first port of call. Increasingly in our hard economic world, the quantity surveyor, acting as construction cost adviser, can take the opportunity to be the first on the scene. Creating a building is a large-scale economic activity before it is a technical one. Many building owners, and virtually all developers, know what they want to spend before they know what they want to build. And any discipline that can offer project management services may approach the customer to offer management services as a very first step in the project.

Deep within the project structure, similar principles operate. Various advisory services can be offered to our own immediate customer. The classic example is of course the supplier or subcontractor who provides the architect or engineer with design advice in exchange for having the product specified or, if for some reason the product cannot be specified, at least having the design prepared in a way that favours the supplier's own product. The increasing complexity of modern buildings, and the ever more complex interaction between components, create more and more opportunity for enterprising specialist firms to develop services that solve problems for their immediate customers and help to ensure a place on the team. But the service has to be good: everything depends on it being offered and delivered by likeable, helpful, competent and energetic people. And the sequence of those adjectives is no accident!

Managing competition

So, we limit competition by trying to get to the client at as early a point as possible in the inception of the project. To interest the client at that point, we have to offer a product that deals with the first problems of setting up the project. At the first approach, clients sometimes ask, 'How did you know we were thinking of...?' The real answer is often that we didn't know. But our market intelligence (in both senses of the word) told us where to look for someone who might just be thinking of.... The more often this happens to us, the more confidence we can place in our market intelligence.

Having arrived first on the scene, we must try to establish a toe-hold in the project. We need an order for some initial item of work. And we must understand the rules by which the client works, to avoid getting into a position where, because we have undertaken a particular consultancy role, we cannot participate in later parts of the work which are our real target. It may be necessary to perform some kind of 'free' service as a starter. Care must be taken with free service. Most of us do not respect what is free! The 'free' front-end service may be best offered as a demonstration of what we can do or perhaps a joint exercise between the two parties to see how we can work together. If we can establish a relationship between partners, both looking for the way forward, so much the better. Working with us must be a pleasurable experience. However good we are, if we are difficult to deal with we have created a big disadvantage for ourselves. It is perfectly possible to be tough and positive and to guard our own interests while maintaining a very friendly relationship with the client.

Ideally, having got on board at or near the inception, we will try to stay there. But if there is to be competition, we must try to ensure that it is conducted on a basis which does not place us at a disadvantage. This is not corrupt. We know that we will do a better job for our client than anyone else will. If we will not do the best job, we must mend our ways: if we do not believe that we will do the best job we should pack up and go home! Our client will follow the path that suits us only if he is convinced that it is right for him. Again we need to 'place ourselves in the position of the customer' and understand the rules and the objectives. What is the objective? The best job? The lowest price? Selection and pricing on a 'publicly accountable basis'? Whatever combination it is, we should look carefully at what we want, and what we can afford to give away. Then we can shape a proposal for competition or negotiation, designed to achieve both our objective and the client's.

Easier said than done? Not necessarily. Assume for example that we are a multi-discipline design and project management firm. What we want is the commission for design and overall project management. The client wants the lowest overall cost; time is important but it is not the primary consideration. We therefore recommend a project structure to the client under which we are commissioned at an early date to prepare fully detailed designs and documentation for obtaining competitive tenders for everything. We recommend the appointment of a quantity surveyor, chosen from a list of three, each of whom has the highest possible reputation for cost management. The quantity surveyor will also act as the client's adviser in settling our fees. We demonstrate our own track record in economic design and effective management. One of the quantity surveyor's main tasks is to 'value engineer' the designs we prepare to ensure that they are the most economic answers to the brief. There is a 'break' provision in both our appointment and that of the quantity surveyor at the point at which firm prices for all the construction have been assembled. This means that we both have a strong incentive to achieve the firm price that the client needs —he could walk away if we do not perform. If this strategy succeeds, we obtain a negotiated commission; our fee is tight because the client has had skilled advice in negotiating it, but it is a profitable fee with enough cost allowed to enable us to do a good job. The client achieves his objective of obtaining keen firm prices because the design has been subject to value engineering and firm prices have been obtained on a fully-developed design which need not change. If the client had been in the public sector, and as concerned with even-handed and accountable tendering as with the lowest price, the emphasis would have been more on the tendering procedure. And it would have been necessary to agree a carefully argued case for the 'single tender' appointment of the two consultants.

A similar result can be achieved in most such situations by writing down our own objectives and those of the client, and then applying commercially creative thinking to devise a way to satisfy both sets of needs. It may be that our client insists on obtaining competition to our own appointment. There are several reasons for going to tender. The most likely is to get a real market price. Another is to be seen to be selecting by fair competition. A third, which is perhaps a special case of the second, is where a favoured firm, perhaps not ourselves, must be seen to be obtaining work in competition. Whatever the reason, if we understand it it helps us to devise a suitable approach. Again, taking into account the client's needs and our own, we can suggest ways forward that meet them both. If we are designers, and more confident that we can produce an economic design than a tight fee, we should suggest competition on designs and budget prices. There could be a contribution to the design costs of the unsuccessful bidders. Some sanction, at a realistic level in terms of the size of the fee, may need to apply if we do not live up to our budget of capital cost.

We know only too well what our needs are. The key is always to understand the client's need, and to shape our approach to ensure that we provide it.

Reading the client's real need

People do not always say what they really mean. And what they say they want sometimes does not reflect their real need. We place ourselves at a competitive advantage if we learn to read the client's real needs, and use our knowledge to shape our offering. This applies not only on the commercial side of things, but also in technical matters connected with the brief and detailed requirements for the work. We must, however, be very careful to avoid the arrogance of telling the client that we know what is best for him. We keep quiet, and use the information rather than declaring it!

Taking the initiative

One of the books recommended for further reading is *Offensive marketing* by Hugh Davidson, subtitled *or how to make your competitors followers*. This must be our aim. We must be alert to every possible opportunity for advantage. It is them or us. If we don't take advantage, our competitors will.

The inside track

In seeking advantage, we must always look for what is called an 'inside track'. Not an 'insider' track, but a shorter route to the objective. 'Strengths and weaknesses' is not only a game to be played at marketing strategy time. It is a deadly serious business tactic, which must be always at the forefront of the competitive mind. At every stage in competition, we must be looking for ways to employ our strengths and exploit the weaknesses of our competitors.

Pricing advantage

The best way of obtaining a price advantage is to be as efficient as possible, to keep our overheads to the minimum and to ensure that our actual costs are as low as they can be, while still providing the appropriate level of service. That should go without saying. But do we always remember it?

In negotiation, we must take care not to kill the goose that lays the golden egg. We have not got the order until the client signs on the dotted line. Clearly, we take advantage of our negotiating position, but if we push our luck to the point at which the client walks away, we have no job.

Put simplistically, the initial price is our unit charge multiplied by the amount of work we do: the rate by the quantity. The final price is affected by other factors that may or may not arise during the execution of the work. We may obtain an initial price advantage either by pricing 'less' work or by pricing it more cheaply.

How can we price less work? In circumstances where we are determining the scope of our own work and making an offer of scope and price, we make quite sure that we understand the extent of the customer's need and the quality required, and we offer only what the customer really wants. That does not mean that we deprive ourselves of some of the work and the client of some of the service. It is perfectly possible to offer a minimum scope at a very attractive price that underlines our efficiency and economy, and to offer alternatives which include very desirable (prefer-ably not essential) extras at separately attractive prices. This is the 'basic model' approach, in which nobody expects to sell the basic model but it is there as an indication that you can actually have a car for under £5000, £20 000 or whatever the going price is. If the scope is already determined, we must make sure that we are pricing and offering only what the client has said he needs. If we think that the specified scope is extravagant or that its purpose could be achieved in a more economical way, we should say so. We must however take care that we have not missed the point: there may be factors we do not understand. And in a competitive tender we must avoid being disqualified for not submitting a conforming bid.

Our eventual payment for the work is not necessarily the tender price; the final account may be different for many reasons. The age-old estimator's technique of tactical pricing of bills of quantity to take advantage of probable changes in scope—price high on the things that are likely to increase and low on the ones that will reduce or disappear—is always valid. But we should not push our luck to the point at which disadvantages in terms of reputation and client relationships outweigh the tactical advantages.

Closing the deal

In a race, the most important metre is the one after the finishing tape! If we don't finish at full pace, someone else will. It is worth repeating that we have not got the order until the client has signed on the dotted line. We must finish hard!

7. Image, identity and brochures

Corporate identity

Each of us has his or her own individual human personality. We express it in many different ways by our behaviour, our appearance and our possessions. As circumstances vary, so does the expression of our personality.

Company directors, architects, clergymen, musicians, teachers, farmers, milkmen and bus conductors each wear the 'uniform' of their calling. The clothes, the hair style, the personal accessories, even the car (or bicycle), combine to suggest the profession and status of the wearer. At leisure, the same individuals may meet in the pub, on the golf course, in the shopping precinct, on the beach, in church, as elected representatives in local governement—or anywhere. There, they may have greater freedom, but most of them will do what is expected of their particular group, expressing their individuality by their behaviour and choice of attire, but usually within an accepted range.

Organisations also have personalities. Like that of individuals, the corporate personality is the substance of the organisation expressed through its behaviour and appearance. This expression of personality can be called 'corporate identity'. In other words, the company's activities, property, products, people and communications combine to give its customers, the general public and of course its employees an impression of what the company is and what its aims are. They form that impression mainly from what they see. A deliberate corporate identity can therefore be created by a skilful visual design applied consistently to everything the company owns, occupies, makes, wears or sends out.

Like an individual, it will be difficult for a firm to achieve its full potential, however good it is, if it does not look the part. Conversely, if the firm is really bad, no amount of cosmetic 'image' treatment will ensure its success. Whether it tries to project itself or not, each organisation has its identity. Whether or not that identity reveals the underlying reality of the organisation in its best light is a matter for careful consideration.

To bring us down to earth, let us consider a small local plumbing firm whose business is to provide maintenance and emergency services for the office and domestic community in an inner London surburb. The firm has two grubby red vans, both of which show the vestiges of their first owner's distinctive livery. The operatives wear greasy brown overalls and carry a dirty canvas bag of tools. 'Is he really going to put that bag down on my bathroom carpet? Even kneeling down in those overalls would be bad enough!' However careful and considerate the plumbers are, the grubby plain van, the greasy overalls and the dirty tool bag all suggest a slovenly job and some incidental damage to finishes and furnishings in its vicinity. How much better it would be if the van were clean and white, with a logo suggesting, diagrammatically, a shining plumber's wrench and some clear bright flowing water. To that we add clean overalls bearing the same logo, a smart case to contain the tools to be taken into the customer's premises, and perhaps a name and slogan on the van suggesting the service that can be obtained by calling the telephone number.

PETER THE PIPER
Pick a Pack of Perfect Plumbers
call 071-123 4567

The difference has a dramatic effect on three separate audiences. The customer no longer views the invaders of domestic or office privacy with dread. They are seen to be people concerned about their own appearance and that of their client's facilities. Passers-by and other drivers, all of whom are potential customers for a local plumber, see and remember the van with its logo and slogan. Whether they remember the telephone number or not, they certainly remember where to look in the *Yellow Pages* when they need a plumber. But another important audience for the new identity, and perhaps the most important, is the employees themselves. The smart uniform, the new interest other people take in the van, the better reception given to them by the customer, all combine to improve their self-perception, their pride in their work and their sense of belonging to the team. Not only do they look better and feel better, they *are* better. The new identity has acted as a catalyst for change, reinforcing the reality it tries to project.

The example of the plumbing firm is very simple in order to make the point, but exactly the same principles apply to any organisation. Indeed, the larger and more complex the organisation, the more necessary it is to define its personality and to impose the means for projection of that personality on the whole diverse entity.

Our projection must show what we are, what we do and how we do it. Peter the Piper is a plumber. He provides the means of hot and cold running water for drinking, washing and heating, where and when it is needed, and not where it is not needed. He is prompt, clean and user-friendly.

The corporate identity centres upon the 'idea' of our business. This idea is the centre point of our marketing strategy. It says to us, first of all, what business we are in and how we see ourselves, and want others to see us, within that business. It has a great deal to do with positioning, as discussed in chapter 2. It is the idea which is the rallying point for the team. The idea underlying Peter the Piper's new identity is associated with the need for fresh water for drinking and washing allied to the risks of employing a plumber. When we need a plumber we need him fast, but his activity, whether in a household or in business premises, is an invasion of our privacy and exposes us to significant risks of mess and of being overcharged. A clean and efficient-looking team, differentiated from grubby-looking competitors, is calculated to give Peter the Piper an edge over the run-of-the-mill competition. The simple identity based on this idea comprises clean vans and accessories, a relevant pictorial logo and a deliberately corny, but very memorable, alliterative name and slogan. In a larger and more complex organisation, this identity would be part of a comprehensive suite of materials, designed to communicate the same message through all visible manifestations of the organisation.

The identity is expressed in a surprisingly small number of elements. These are basically names, symbols, colours and lettering. The naming issue is perhaps the most significant, and in an existing organisation it is often the most contentious. Should we continue to use our old name, by which we are well known in our existing marketplace, or should we create a new name with which we can build a new reputation? Should the name reflect our history, ownership or some other internal factor? Or should it describe what we do? 'Joe Bloggs Limited' or 'Peter the Piper'?

After the name, the next critical element is the logotype or 'logo'. This is the symbol in which we choose to sum up our identity. The UK construction industry has some very well known examples. Taylor Woodrow's tug-of-war team is one of the most descriptive. Bovis' hummingbird is more subtly symbolic. Tarmac's Ts are memorable and ubiquitous. Trafalgar House reflects its shipping interests in its set of three pennants. Logos in general range from the totally abstract symbol, which becomes associated with the company only by use and promotion, to that which carries an obvious message about the nature of the organisation. It is a matter of style.

Most organisations have a house colour or system of colours. In terms of formal corporate identity, it is important that these colours should be appropriate and consistently applied. And finally there is lettering: once again, it is important that typefaces are chosen to suit the style of the organisation. It is common, for example, for building firms to project an 'old established' image using old-English styles of typeface.

Our identify is aimed at more separate audiences than one might think. The first and most obvious audience is the customer and potential customer. But this is by no means the only one. We saw that Peter the Piper's workforce were encouraged and motivated by the firm's new image. The staff can be the most important audience for the identity. Many corporate identity programmes are aimed primarily at motivating the staff. But it does not stop there. We must remember that we are also seen by a host of other groups, all of whom we must keep favourably disposed towards us in one way or another. Within the staff group, we must not ignore potential recruits, pensioners, the employees in their corporate form as trade unions, and so on. A public company has to consider its existing shareholders, other potential investors and those who, privately or through public media, influence or advise them. Larger organisations must consider how government sees them.

Not only does the identity have a very wide variety of audiences, but it is expressed in many different ways on a large number of different items. The most obvious group of items is those whose purpose is communication itself. Starting with the office letterhead, we can add invoices, business cards, press notice sheets and other similar items. This group includes all forms of advertising, whether commercial or for recruitment.

Another group pertains to the places at which we do business. Offices, factories and warehouses are the fixed places, but in construction our most visible place of business is often the site. Identity here is of great importance. Overall control of the site identity is the prerogative of only one of the many organisations involved: perhaps the building owner. But identification of our people through hard hats and overalls, consistent designs applied to site equipment, sign boards and site offices can differentiate them from their less good-looking rivals. Despite our systematic efforts to obtain business through 'formal' marketing activities, we all know that just being there and looking good is an important source of enquiries.

Our passer-by audience is often inconvenienced by our operation. How many contractors show their name visibly on the roadworks site throughout the period of frustrating traffic chaos; saying, in effect, 'Here we are, this is who is holding you up!' and then remove the signs, forgoing the opportunity of saying, 'Look at this amazing new road we've built which gets you from A to B without the delay and frustration you used to suffer!'?

The third group of items consists of the product itself. Sir Christopher Wren is still known by the great buildings he designed and built. Who even knows whether his firm had a logo?

Peter the Piper was a small firm with a single identity. If the original 'Peter the Piper' had succeeded and had gone on to sell his controlling interest to a major holding group, that identity would have become part of a much larger one. Such a group with diverse interests has to decide whether it should be identified as a single monolithic entity, or as a single entity with a number of quite separate activities, or whether the main corporation should allow the individual susidiaries or products to take the limelight and develop their independent identities. Much depends on the sectors through which the group is ranged and the amount of integration between the various subsidiaries. There are examples of all three types in the construction industry. One real issue in construction, of course, is the cross-contracting and subcontracting which is an essential part of day-to-day business. Groups who fear that their main contracting competitors may not like a competitor's name displayed boldly on their site may opt for the independent type of identity for their subcontractor subsidiaries. This is an important commercial decision, and must be taken as such.

The graphic design of corporate identities and their components is a specialist, skilled activity. All too often, firms in the construction industry allow designers from other disciplines loose on their corporate identity or other communications material. Why not, by the same reasoning, have a graphic designer determine the arrangements for the new head office building? Powerful graphics and desktop publishing packages can also become a snare and a delusion. Confusion between skill on the excellent computer package and skill in the design of communcations material may lead to disaster.

Finally on corporate identity—if we make changes, they must be positive and effective. Regular tinkering with identity confuses all the audiences, often to the point of irritation. When new material has to be produced, we must ensure that it is designed as a rational extension of our suite of existing material. If we are to make a change, particularly if it is something radical like a change of name or the introduction of a new logo, we must first count the cost of launching it with sufficient vigour to make it stick! How many times have we come across people who explain their organisation by reference to what it used to be called?

The roles of brochures

The job of a brochure is to communicate. Our job is to decide what it should communicate, to whom and how. It may seem unnecessary to make such a simplistic statement about an everyday item like a brochure: surely a brochure just explains what we do. But does it? In general, our client is not very interested in what we do. He is interested in what we are going to do for him, that is what benefit he will gain from our activity. Our instinct in preparing a brochure is to list and to illustrate the work we have done and, if we think a little more about it, to schedule the products and services we provide. In some cases this may be what is required. But we will only discover that when we have, yet again, 'placed ourselves in the position of the customer' at whom this brochure is aimed.

Our market is segmented. That is we separate our target areas of business into blocks called 'segments' which contain groups of customers who require similar products and who can be approached similarly with similar arguments. The concept of segmentation is purpose-made for brochures. If we have prepared our marketing strategy thoroughly, we should be able to review our segmentation and consider each segment of our target market as a candidate for its own brochure.

As brochures can cost a great deal of money, we must, in the light of our marketing strategy, agree a brochure strategy and budget. Not to do so will inevitably mean that sooner or later we shall come across a need for a brochure which cannot be ignored and for which we have no money. And by an inevitable law of perversity, we shall find at the very same moment a pile of other brochures, on which we have recently lavished a great deal of time and money, stacked mouldering in the cupboard under the stairs.

Segmentation can be defined as the division of the market or of customers into categories according to their buying habits. In chapter 2 we saw that this means the identification of both the products they are predisposed to buy and the messages that are likely to persuade them to buy those products. In a design-and-build market, for example, our key client groups may be private sector industrial, commercial property developers, public sector local government and public sector central government. Each of these groups buys a separate range of design-and-build products, or packages of service. And each has different aims in considering this route to obtaining a new building. This means that quite different messages are required for each group.

The industrial client for a relatively simple factory building may want speed, predictability, least initial capital cost, single responsibility, minimum involvement of valuable executive time, and so on. The property developer is more likely to be sold on the skill of the designer in achieving a design which meets his commercial objectives for the development; pre-contract costs at the contractor's risk; commitment to fixed cost for the firm brief he is able to give, a track record of meeting programme dates, etc. A local authority may be looking for a design-and-build contract wrapped up into a clever property deal which provides a new civic facility in exchange for the grant of certain other property opportunities to the developer—if cash changes hands if flows towards the authority. Public sector clients will be particularly concerned with propriety and accountability, and within those constraints may be looking for a deal which provides as much as possible for a limited budget and with limited supervising resources. Clearly, the packaging and description of services and the selling messages to be contained in brochures will be different for each of these groups. In some cases there may be common ground, but in general only the most superficial material will appeal to all groups.

Brochure strategy

Brochures are one of the sets of tools available to us for the implementation of our marketing strategy. The brochure strategy must therefore come from the marketing strategy. Indeed, in writing our marketing strategy, we may well consider committing ourselves to the outline of the brochure strategy while the arguments for our segmentation are clearly in our minds.

Each brochure must have a clear purpose and a target audience. It must be clear what that audience is to be told and why. We must consider our brochures as a complete set, and make sure that they are compatible and consistent. In taking this overall view, we allow ourselves to review the brochure activity against whatever budget we have set. This will enable us from the outset to establish clear priorities and to spend our brochure money where it is likely to have most effect in helping to generate profitable business. There are always unforeseen opportunities which require some sort of publication in mid-budget. It is wise, as in all budgeting, to allow a modest contingency for such eventualities.

The most important brochure issued by any organisation is its annual report. In a market-led company, the annual report is as much a marketing document as it is a statement of financial and associated corporate data. Its main audience in a publicly quoted company is, of course, investors and their advisers. But it has an equally important role in demonstrating the financial substance of the organisation to customers, bankers, subcontractors, suppliers, trade unions and emloyees, all of whom need to know the strength of the organisation they are dealing with. Many large organisations issue supplementary versions of the annual report, for example a summary document for staff and small private shareholders. In marketing terms, the parent company annual report can be a valuable prop for a small subsidiary which needs to demonstrate that it has the strength of the family around it.

The need for different kinds of brochure depends on specific markets and our strategy for approaching them. We may need a hierarchy of brochures for our independent company or for our trading subsidiary within a larger group. At the top of the hierarchy is the corporate brochure, which fulfils some of the functions of the annual report. Everyone feels the need for a corporate brochure: it gives us the comfort of knowing what we are about. It is of great value when we are not sure which of our services the potential client may need. It is likely, however, to be the most expensive brochure and the one most difficult to get right. In considering our brochure strategy we must be sure that we really need a corporate brochure and, if we do, that we define its purpose clearly and design it carefully to fulfil that purpose.

The second set of brochures in the hierarchy is the group directed at our segmented market. If our segmentation is good, these are the easiest to get right. We have a clear message to give to a well-defined audience, and we should have thought about both audience and message long before we came to design the brochures!

Our third set of items of literature fulfils special tactical purposes within the overall marketing function. These may be small leaflets for sending through the post if our market sector requires that. They may be special items for issue from an exhibition stand or at a special event of some kind. They may celebrate the completion of a project and, among other uses, form part of the press and guest pack at the official opening. These brochures are the most difficult to control. In particular, the project brochure, which may be initiated by an individual project manager and may be paid for by the project estimate rather than from a central budget, may well make an important contribution to the organisation, but it may equally be part of a maverick effort to bypass central strategy.

In summary: our brochure strategy must create a document or a suite of documents, each of which is directed quite specifically at achieving one or more of the aims of our marketing strategy. Brochures are too important and too expensive to be left to chance, or to be dealt with on an ad hoc basis.

Brochure design

The job of a brochure is to communicate. In designing it we must make sure that it does precisely that, and that it communicates precisely what we wish to say to the audience for which it is designed.

One of the most common mistakes is to try to put too much into the brochure. We are keen to communicate; we try to communicate all we know in a few pages. In particular, we may use too much copy. Some brochures, of course, must communicate a great deal of detailed information which must be set out in a long text. However, these are exceptions. We must decide this matter as we review the aim and audience of the brochure.

Again, we come back to the need to place ourselves in the position of the customer. How do *we* respond to a brochure when it arrives on our desk? The first thing we do is to look at it and, without even thinking about it, assess its quality. The first impression is very important. The quality of the material, the overall design, the print, the colour and the reproduction of any photograph that may be on the cover give us an instant impression of the brochure and, therefore, of the company that has sent or handed it to us. If it survives this first inspection, we look through it. We look at the pictures and the headlines. These should give us the whole message of the brochure in the form of a summary impression. Most of us will not begin to read the copy unless we are interested in what we see. In designing any brochure, these must therefore be clear priorities.

The first priority is the overall design and suitability for its purpose of the document itself. It does not follow that the most expensive and most glossy brochure is the most effective. The positioning of the brochure must reflect the positioning of the product and the company, and the expectations of its audience. The corporate brochure of a great multi-national construction group, whose customers are other world-class corporations and the rulers and governments of great and wealthy nations, must be of the highest quality. At the other end of the scale, if the builders' merchant's catalogue of sale-price, store-soiled drainage goods, sent by second-class post to all the jobbing builders in the locality, appeared on anything other than photocopied sheets of modest quality A4 paper, neither the supplier nor the goods would have any credibility. There is a whole range of possibilities between these two.

The second priority is the design of the message for first reading. The customer, in general, has no interest whatever in what we do for its own sake. Our potential customer wants to know what is in it for him. What are the benefits of doing business with us, or of accepting the proposition we are making? These must be spelt out in headlines, in punch lines with 'bullets', or in very short sections of copy placed in such a way as to make them impossible to ignore.

The third priority is the copy. Unless the brochure is the rare one whose main purpose is to provide a great deal of detailed information, the copy should be the minimum necessary to achieve our objective, which in itself should be limited. Bear in mind that a significant proportion of recipients will not get as far as reading the copy. But the text must be very carefully written to make quite sure that, when it is read, it cannot convey any wrong impression and does not contradict any of the messages offered by higher-level reading of the brochure.

There is always a temptation for architects to design their own or the company's brochures and for other professionals—technical people, commercial managers or company lawyers—to write the copy. There are horses for courses. Many architects are no doubt extremely good at designing brochures, but it is not necessarily so. Experts writing their own copy tend to protect their own expertise. We should employ competent specialists to design and write our brochures. By all means have the in-house experts check the accuracy of what has been done, but little will be achieved if the visual impact of the brochure owes more to the principles of building design than of communications. And, if the lawyers write the sales copy like a building contract, it will repel rather than attract.

Uses and abuses of brochures

Other than the simple 'mailer' which is posted either to a very large number of target customers of whom we expect a very small percentage to respond, or to a captive group of preconditioned willing recipients, as is, for example, a mail order catalogue, brochures in themselves do not sell.

We sell construction industry services mainly by developing relationships. Brochures in general, therefore, are but one means of communicating our marketing message. We must not expect to gain much merely by placing a brochure on a target client's desk. The main value of brochures is in support of discussions and correspondence. They serve as a reminder of personal contact.

New or updated brochures should be sent to established contacts. The brochure itself is a reminder, and the opportunity to send it is a good excuse for keeping in touch with the potential client. In most cases, brochures should not be sent on their own to a new cold contact. Whether or not to enclose a brochure with a sales letter aimed at generating a first meeting is a matter for consideration. Chapter 5 suggests that a letter without a brochure seems more personal and is more likely to obtain the required meeting. Take the brochure to the meeting, and hand it over after the discussion.

Other presentation material

Chapter 10 deals with the use of overhead and 35 mm slides, tape/slide presentations, video, film, flip charts etc. at interviews and meetings. A few principles concerning these media are worth mentioning here.

We must ensure that our corporate identity envelops all of our communication materials. The company logo on the front sheet of the flip chart never fails to impress. Standard margins and the logo or company imprint on the basic overhead slide material make for uniformity. If we use tape/slide presentations regularly, the choice of the recorded voice-over should take account of the possible need to match job-specific material to the standard material already recorded. Voice-over recording is a skilled technique, and should in general be left to the professionals.

Video is becoming an increasingly important medium, both in support of face-to-face presentations and for independent submission for private viewing by the recipient. With skill and application, it can be one of our most effective means of communication. People are accustomed to receiving a high proportion of their 'selling messages' through TV advertising, and are therefore conditioned to the medium. Conditioning is a two-edged sword, however: the material used in TV advertising is made at a very high cost per minute and is of the highest technical standard. Any selling material we offer will be judged against that standard. If we use video, it must be done professionally with messages carefully prepared for the specific audience. Joe from the design office must keep his VHS camcorder for technical material.

8. Secondary Activities

Support for marketing

Anyone who has ever had responsibility for a marketing budget knows that few things people like to do have not at some time been justified by calling them 'marketing' and charging the marketing budget. So, if you are a horse-racing fan, take a box at the races, or even sponsor a race. If you enjoy the ballet, or cricket, or rugby, get some tickets. If you sail, take the day off and fill the galley with goodies for a merry day at sea—or in the marina if the weather is bad. If you are into aeroplanes, take a stand at the air show. If you want to compete with Pirelli to publish a collectable calendar, employ a top photographer and produce one. So long as you involve some customers, charge it up to marketing!

This is great if you enjoy it, great if the company can afford it, even greater if it happens to do us some good. But if we are really supporting our marketing activity, we must think of these things from a different perspective. What are our marketing objectives? To which business friends do we need to be closer? Are they able to participate in what we plan without breaking their own rules for the conduct of business? If we attend an exhibition, will our customers be there, and are we likely to meet any that could not be met more satisfactorily and economically by approaching them directly? Do our giveaways act as a constant reminder of our existence to people we want to remember us, or do they end up decorating the homes and offices of people with whom we have no connection at all?

Many secondary marketing activities add valuable support to our direct efforts. But they must be planned, they must be purposeful and, as far as possible, we must monitor their effectiveness.

Entertaining

Entertaining is a very important part of the process of building business relationships. However, potential difficulties make this an area that requires firm but sensitive management. These difficulties relate to control, purpose and value for money. A receipt from an expensive restaurant and a likely-sounding name on the claim: that gravy train is ridden by many managers with responsibility for customer relationships and a so-called 'expense account'. A clear policy is required for personal entertaining. Who is required to do it? Should the entertainment be approved in advance or in retrospect, and by whom? What is the policy on quality and venue? And the nature of the entertainment? What about the nightclub after dinner? And what about the individual, who exists in every organiation, who always comes back the next morning and says that the client got so involved with the hostess...?

The purpose of entertaining is to improve personal relationships, the better to conduct business. We all remember the apocryphal choirboys' cricket team who were given a fiver by the vicar to use in trying to improve their competitive performance. He was not very pleased when he learned that they had given it to the umpire! Whether we give fivers to the umpire or not is a matter for our own business and personal judgement. For most businesses, however, there is a recognisable boundary between proper hospitality and activities that may be perceived as calculated to achieve an objective which is less than legitimate.

Two thoughts about hospitality: getting to know the client's spouse is of inestimable value in developing a personal business relationship. Many people accept corporate hospitality mainly to meet their host's other guests.

Sponsorship

An entire industry is now dedicated to the bestowal and reception of sponsorship. Gone are the days when the classic race was known simply by its own name or by the name of the course where it was run, or when the Cup Final was the Cup Final. Events are now known by the names of their sponsor, and sponsorship has become an important source of financial support for these events. Sponsorship may be of local, regional, national or international events. Many events create valuable parallel opportunities for entertainment.

There is no shortage of opportunities to provide sponsorship. The question is whether or not it provides a measurable return in a particular case. One well-known razor manufacturer is said to have discontinued sponsorship of a cricket competition because its name had become more associated in the public mind with cricket than with shaving.

Certain products, perhaps leisurewear or sports gear directly associated with the sponsored events, may gain a direct commercial benefit from the sponsorship. But, in general, sponsorship by the construction industry must be one of those 'nice to do' things at the bottom of the marketing budget, for spending the money that gets lost in the rounding up.

Exhibitions

Exhibitions are expensive to take part in, and the total cost is not always apparent at the first estimate. Apart from the rental of the space in the hall and the cost of designing and putting up the stand, there are a range of incidental costs. It always takes more people than you think to keep the stand manned effectively. Once word goes round that you have a stand at an exhibition which is of interest to the other people in the office, they all want free tickets and the day off to be there. There are the support costs for the attenders, travel expenses, hotel costs and the like. Hotels near major exhibitions are always expensive. The cheap ones are booked from year to year, and the expensive ones suspend their discount arrangements when they have full occupancy during the exhibition. Regular use of mobile telephones on the stand can add a significant cost.

Having estimated the probable cost, what are we going to gain? Is the exhibition targeted at potential customers? Many construction industry exhibitions are targeted at and attended by people from within the construction industry itself. That is perfect if we are in a business—and more of us are than are not—which serves the industry itself. But if our targets are among the industry's external clientele, we have to consider how many of them will actually attend the exhibition. We may be wasting our time and money. One important test is whether our major competitors are there. If they are not, it may be because our customers are not, but it may also be because they have not recognised the value of being there! If we are not to be followers rather than leaders, we must make up our own minds on the basis of our own commercial interests. If we are right, our competitors will soon follow us.

Giveaways

The right giveaway goodies can yield benefits quite disproportionate to their cost. There are many small items which cost only a few pounds, or even less, which the recipient will use for years and which will continue to remind him of the donor's firm—and even give him the telephone number at his fingertips.

9. Press and publicity

External communications are very much a part of marketing. In a market-led organisation, all communications with external audiences are affected by market considerations, and the whole range of communication media is available to support specific marketing efforts. It does not follow, however, that all external relations should be under the control of the marketing department. In some areas communications must be seen to be of a 'corporate' nature, and therefore above the day-to-day business of drumming up new work. This applies, for example, to the relationship of a quoted company with the City and to that of a multinational organisation with governments. Whether or not external relations are the responsibility of the marketing director is a matter for individual company choice, based on the company's structure and circumstances.

'Above the line' and 'below the line'

These expressions are widely used in advertising and public relations. Precise usage varies, but in general activities described as 'above the line' are both paid for and visible. This includes all kinds of paid advertising, rental of space at exhibitions, and so on. In activities which are 'below the line', the medium of transmission is not necessarily paid for and the communication may or may not be overt. The issue of a press release in the expectation of a favourable report in a newspaper is an example of 'below the line' activity. Our 'above the line' budget has to bear the full cost of the communication and, because we are paying for it, it is under our control. 'Below the line' publicity is 'free' except for costs incurred in preparing and placing the material. A professional public relations consultant provides a 'below the line' service. Each type has its place, according to our particular needs.

The role of advertising

Effective advertising is an expensive game. In chapters 2 and 3 we saw that in each market segment we have a set of target customers, specific

109

products to offer them and an argument to predispose them to buy th products from us. How do we reach them to communicate that argument

If the target customers are 500 managing directors of companies of certain size in selected industries, we can identify them easily as ind viduals and make a personal approach. If our potential customer may be for example, any one from among 100 000 chartered civil engineers although their names and addresses may be accessible from the publishe list of members of the Institution of Civil Engineers, a direct approac may not be cost-effective. If we decide to advertise to reach those civi engineers, we will consider which media they are most likely to see. Mos will see television. Most will read one or more of the broadshee newspapers. But so will large numbers of other people. And the hig circulation or audience figures may mean that the advertising will b expensive. All civil engineers and relatively few others receive *New Civi Engineer*. It is likely therefore that if we were advertising to reach civi engineers, *NCE* would be the chosen medium.

Our purpose is to reach our target segmented customers in order to pu an argument to them. We must consider all the means of communicatio available to us, including advertising, and devise the most cost-effectiv mix.

Advertising is used in marketing in two separate ways. As in sellin cornflakes, it may prepare the customer for a point-of-sale or face-to-fac decision. That is, it is part of the message but not the part that closes th sale. Cornflakes advertising sends us to the supermarket humming th jingle. We see our 'sunshine breakfast' on the shelf and, before we knov it, it is in the trolley. When the architect answers the telephone and hear the representative mention the name of a plastic-coated cladding system he immediately recognises it—the product is advertised in *Architects Journal*.

The other kind of advertising solicits enquiries directly. The colou supplements are full of glossy advertisements making amazing offers o compact discs or leisure clothing. These make it easy for the customer b providing a cut-out coupon; you can even write in your credit car number. Better still, you can call a 24-hour telephone number and giv your order and your credit card details, at midnight if you wish. The sam approach works in the business-to-buisness situation as long as it is th result of the carefully worked out scheme for approaching the chose market segment.

Life is not always simple. In many cases our advertising may aim botl to support other activity and to obtain some direct responses. Man companies say that they advertise 'to raise awareness' or 'as part of ou general public relations campaign'. There is nothing wrong with either o these reasons for advertising, but there must be a clearly understoo purpose and a defined audience, and the advertising must be consisten with the company's specific marketing activity. Take, for example, Conglomerate plc which owns Amazing Windows Limited whose product sells under the brand name 'Warma Window'. The Warma Window is heavily advertised in the trade press. Awareness advertising of Conglomerate or Amazing will do little for the branded product, and may confuse potential customers. Conglomerate plc may have good reason to raise its profile with investors, bankers and other financial institutions, but Amazing Windows will certainly confuse matters if it seeks to raise its profile in competition with the window brand name. In this situation, unless Amazing has a range of brand names, each offered in its segment of the market, corporate identity considerations may suggest that the company should call itself by the brand name.

In this brief outline of advertising, it is worth mentioning in passing some related issues which, although relatively trivial, can give rise to misunderstanding. Local and regional newspapers issue special supplements to commemorate the opening of new buildings or public works. The participants in the project are invited to advertise. Such advertising is more likely to be a matter of courtesy to the client and to the local community than of direct marketing value. We must decide on that basis whether to spend the relatively small sum involved. Some companies budget the cost as part of the project estimate rather than as a marketing overhead. Its expenditure may therefore be under the control of the project manager. There must be a means of technical control to ensure that this minor advertising is compatible with corporate identity and with central advertising strategy.

The national press issues specialist supplements, sometimes on a relatively ad hoc basis. Whether or not the supplement is actually issued may depend on the advertising revenue target being achieved. Last-minute bargain offers are often made by the space salesmen. These opportunities cost real money. We must take care not to be seduced into expensive advertising that we would not have undertaken given the opportunity for mature consideration when preparing our marketing plan.

There are numerous established directories in which an entry supported by an appropriate advertisement can bring direct opportunities for many sectors of business. There are others which at best may be poor value for money, or at worst may have a slim chance of reaching their stated audience. Beware, and check the credentials of the directory before making a commitment.

Selecting an advertising agency

Advertising is a sophisticated business, and a great deal of money can be spent on it. We must be sure that we know what we are trying to say, and to whom we are trying to say it, before committing ourselves. Only we can decide that. And we need the professional support of a competent advertising agency with experience in our sector. Choosing an agency is not easy. There are the very large agencies with specialist departments; their resources are essential for large campaigns. There are many smaller firms which spin out of and back into the big ones on a regular basis. Advertising people are by definition communicators; they sell aggressively. But the industry has a strong tradition of making a 'pitch' in competition for a new 'account'.

Starting from scratch, we may know little about advertising. We do, however, know what our marketing objectives are, and we have decided that advertising is an option. We can learn from the agencies as they compete for our account. But we must remember that, like us, the amount of work the agency will do to secure the account depends on the size of the account and the amount of competition.

Start by writing a simple marketing brief which says what we intend to achieve. Say what is known about the target market, its size and nature and our present involvement in it. Describe the product and the argument with which we intend to sell it. There should be some information about price, perhaps just a statement of our price position relative to known competitors. Say what part we expect advertising to play in the campaign. The brief should, in general, stop short of suggesting to the agency what advertising is required. About one page will be enough at this stage. Depending on the size of the campaign, it could be sent to a dozen or more agencies inviting them to make a preliminary submission for selection to a short list of firms to make a presentation.

On the basis of the first submissions, invite three or four firms to present. In judging the presentations, remember that they are advertising agencies. On the one hand, expect a very polished performance and judge accordingly. On the other hand, try to look behind the gloss for the substance of the firm. Confidentiality is important at all stages. Agencies have Chinese walls, but we should avoid our competitors' agencies if possible. Advertising, even on a small scale, is a high-profile activity. It is prudent to invite a reasonably high level of our own management to sit in on the presentations.

Relations with the press

A few column inches can do us untold good or harm. A brief report on television will be seen by millions of people. There are matters about which we are sensitive, perhaps with good cause. There are events in our day-to-day business which we really would like people to know about.

Good relations with the press and other media are very important. If we are on good terms with the appropriate journalists and reporters, they will probably call us to check the facts of a story about us before writing it up. And on the positive side, our efforts to secure favourable publicity for day-to-day business activities are more likely to succeed if our relations with the fourth estate are in good shape.

Take a look at a national daily newspaper, *The Daily Telegraph* or the *Financial Times* for example. It goes to press every day. Today's paper may contain a quarter of a million words of live news; so will tomorrow's. The journalists' task is a mammoth one, and before today's paper is put to bed they are beginning to think of tomorrow's. Critics of the press say that whenever there is an item they know about, it is always mis-reported. Looking at it from the contrary point of view, what is more remarkable is that the papers come out on time, day in day out, with so much material in them.

In dealing with the press, there are two things to remember. First, most newspapers and most journalists are very anxious to get it right. Second, with all that space to fill, the press is hungry for worthwhile news. By recognising these two facts and by organising ourselves to communicate properly with the media we have a good chance of avoiding unjust reports while getting coverage for positive, newsworthy information about our business activities. We took the example of a national broadsheet daily newspaper, but local or regional newspapers, weekly technical journals and daily news programmes on national, regional and local radio and broadcast or cable television are all in the same position.

We must make sure that the media know how to contact us. Most large companies have a press office, staffed with professional specialists. Smaller companies may nominate a director to handle relations with the media. Other organisations find it convenient to share facilities by employing a public relations company to work on their behalf. Whichever way, the arrangements must be clear and the spokesmen well briefed on appropriate matters of general policy and of current potential interest.

There are many excellent public relations firms, but the charlatans are there too. *Caveat emptor*! As with any consultant, it is essential that clear terms of reference and the basis for payment are firmly agreed in advance. If the main requirement is to react to press approaches, the agency must be briefed and must know how to obtain additional briefing at any time of the day or night. If there is a promotional element in the agency's role, be it only to sitmulate our own managers to identify newsworthy material for use by the agency to create press notices, or to arrange events, sponsorship, entertainment of the press etc., it must be precisely defined. Not only may the fees we pay for the agency's services run away with us, but disbursements, our external costs, may get really out of control.

We should have an internal system to flag up matters that could be of interest to the press and are therefore potential topics for a press release.

There are plenty there when you begin to look. Prominent people are always newsworthy. The mayor opening a new building is of interest to the local paper, as the Secretary of State for Transport opening a new length of motorway is to the nationals. We should identify where we have used new methods, the creation of new and interesting products, exceptional performance by the company or an individual. There are surprises and paradoxes. We can sometimes create news by organising events. And so on.

When we offer material to the press, there are several ways of approaching them. These include, for example, issuing a press release, calling a press conference, arranging a private briefing, inviting the press to an event, or a key individual giving a press interview. Selection of the media for any one of these approaches is important. If one journal or TV channel is likely to do best for us, there is a case for giving the information to it on an exclusive basis. However, repeated and undue favouritism may engender unsympathetic handling of news about us by the favoured journal's competitors. If we issue press releases, they must be printed on paper that shows immediately what it is and who it is from. The journalist's desk is covered in paper, and will have competing press releases on it each day. Ours should be well designed to command attention. Its heading should say 'Press Information from . . .' and it should start with a suggested headline. At the foot of the page or on the back, there should be a section of small print under a heading such as 'Notes for Editors' which gives some general background on the organisation, and always an individual to contact for further information. If the individual is accessible around the clock, so much the better.

Another approach to obtaining coverage in periodicals is to mobilise the talents of our own experts. Well-written articles about projects or technical matters of interest are welcomed by the technical journals. If the expert does not have the skill to write an article, a freelance journalist can be brought in to put the expert's know-how into readable prose.

External audiences other than customers

In planning external communications or PR we should remember that in addition to our potential customers there are many other groups with whom we expect to communicate favourably. These include our own staff who will see the results just like anyone else and will take twice as much interest. Shareholders, trade unions, pensioners and potential recruits must be taken into account. If we are a quoted company or a significant force in our industry, the City in the form of bankers, analysts and other investment institutions will take an interest in our affairs. Our competitors will have their ears to the ground. And depending on our size and significance, the Government itself may want to know what we are about.

Public relations agencies and projects

The public relations agency is becoming more common. We have seen its potential value in relation to our day-to-day press activity, if we choose that particular route. But PR can be a very nebulous area, and people will try to justify all sorts of quite expensive activities in its dubious pursuit. Suffice it to say here that, insofar as it is associated with marketing, it must have a purpose consistent with our marketing strategy and any costs incurred must be considered in our overall budgeting of costs to seek new business.

At an advanced level in marketing we may need to influence a wide range of interests in connection with a major project we are promoting. We may need to discover and influence the views of groups ranging from the local population and local industry up to government ministers and other politicians with local or sectional interests. There are specialist agencies who concentrate on this kind of work.

10. Meetings, interviews and negotiations

Building relationships to obtain new business involves a lot of meetings. Many of them are critical, in that they result in a decision about our future involvement in the work or otherwise. It is therefore worth taking a little time to consider some important aspects of client meetings. Chapter 5 suggested how to tackle an initial meeting with a potential customer: this chapter offers some food for thought on meetings in general. There is a brief section on visual aids. We consider the specific case of a 'set-piece' presentation for a selection interview. And we conclude with a few notes on negotiation.

Meetings

If we are to spend time at a meeting, it is worth improving the effectiveness of that time by investing a little more of our time in preparing for it. If the meeting is an important one, this will increase the chance of a successful outcome; if our preparation leads us to the view that the meeting is not important, then we may think again about holding it.

Preparation

The first step is to define our objective for the meeting. What do we want to achieve? We should visualise the end of the meeting: to what do we want to have obtained agreement, what do we want to have discovered, of what do we want to have persuaded others, what arrangements do we want to have made? We should write these objectives down, whether the meeting is under our own or someone else's control. If it is our own meeting, we should decide whether our objectives will be served by preparing an agenda and issuing it either in advance or at the meeting. An advance agenda gives the other participants time to prepare. Is that to our advantage in this situation?

As well as considering our own objectives, we should look at the likely position of the other participants. What are their objectives? What objections will they raise to what we are trying to do? Can we achieve what we want by joining forces with one of the other parties and working together to a common end? If so, should we come to an arrangement before the meeting? It all sounds only too obvious, but most of us do not think of doing it, even for the most important meetings.

At the meeting

Whether in the chair or not, there is a great deal we can do to manage the meeting towards our objectives. The technique of 'chairing' the meeting from one side is a valuable one to learn, but if we do this we must do it inconspicuously and work hard to make sure that we have the support of most of the other participants, particularly the chairman. This can be done by always appearing to be helpful and constructive and supporting the chair. We must take great care not to seen as an unacceptable dominator of the meeting! That would be counterproductive. We should keep our objectives in front of us, and look for opportunities to persuade others very gently that these objectives are also theirs. If we look like losing, we should have some alternative targets as a fall-back. At the end of the meeting or after each key stage, we should make quite sure that any agreement we think has been made which is to our advantage is restated clearly for the whole meeting to hear. It is remarkable how often different parties at the same meeting believe that different things have been agreed.

After the meeting

After the meeting we should privately take stock of what has been achieved, and make some brief informal notes to ensure that if minutes are produced we have a record against which to compare them. We should decide on and take any action we regard as necessary to confirm, repair or amend what has transpired at the meeting.

Presentation materials

Chapter 7 refers to the wide range of visual and audiovisual techniques and equipment that are available to support our communications at meetings and presentations. These include overhead and 35 mm slides, tape/slide presentations, video, film, flip charts and so on. With modern equipment, almost all presentation material can be prepared in-house using a desktop computer with a graphics package. As standards must be high, great care must be taken with the quality of design and production. The most common mistake is to believe that the keyboard buff, who is not a designer, can use the power of the graphics package as a substitute for design capability. The opposite is the case: the more powerful the package, the greater is the need for skilled design input. If in doubt, don't risk failure; call in a professional. All material we produce should be consistent with whatever corporate identity (see chapter 7) we have adopted.

35 mm slides

A carousel of 35 mm transparencies in 2" × 2" mounts is, for many presentation purposes, a good balance between the sometimes competing requirements for quality, flexibility and economy. Photographs and graphic material can be mixed. Individual presentations can be tailored by selecting from a library of slides established for the purpose. Experience suggests that such a library should be under the control of someone who will guard it jealously and ensure the return of the slides after use. It is very easy, in the moment of emotional 'high' after a successful presentation, to forget to reclaim your carousel from the projectionist! With modern cameras and film we can all make good slides. We should remember, however, that professional standards begin where those of an amateur with an autofocus finish; for important slides we should take advantage of the creative skill and production quality of professional work. As desktop technology advances, the equipment to prepare our captions and graphics is more likely to be available in-house. This means that material can be prepared quickly and economically, but again we must consider quality.

Tape/slide presentations

Linking and controlling the slides with an audio tape is one stage slicker than manual slide changing and a live statement. This is worth doing if we have a standard message or if we are willing to spend the time required to edit bespoke material into our basic presentaion. Tape/slide comes into its own where we can use two or three projectors, usually in a fixed location, possibly with back projection; the corporate statement in the boardroom to head-office visitors, for example. The choice of the recorded voice-over is important: this is an area where a trained speaking voice, or even a well known TV or radio voice, can make a lot of difference for a relatively small cost. Job-specific material need not have the same voice, but it should be of reasonable quality and suitable for the material.

Overhead slides

Overhead 'foils' or 'acetates' are valuable for captions, text, tables of figures and diagrams. They are easily prepared in-house with the simplest computer graphics, or even extra large word processor lettering. Most A4 film can be used in a photocopier or laser printer, but check the label on the film and the machine manufacturer's instructions. Some film is not suitable for photocopying; some will melt at the temperatures inside the laser printer. We should consider using standard stock material with pre-printed margins, logo or company imprint. Alternatively, the standard format could be kept in a computer graphics file and printed each time with the actual material.

Video

This is the growing medium: as technology develops and becomes cheaper and more accessible, the scope widens dramatically. Still or movie photography can be combined with simple text, tables, figures (the ubiquitous pie chart) or high quality graphics material linked to CAD. A design presentation that includes a 'walk through'—a three-dimensional video of the drawings—cannot fail to impress. Professional standards are important. We should avoid amateur video photography for all but purely technical material.

Flip charts

Amid all this high-tech presentation, we should not ignore our old friend the flip chart. A large copy of the company logo on the front sheet may add a little style.

Formal interviews and presentations

The selection interview is now very much a fact of life. Professionals, main contractors and subcontractors in turn are invited to attend to make a presentation and to answer questions posed by the potential employer. Our performance at the interview will determine whether we live to fight another day. It is a sudden-death contest, and careful preparation is essential to ensure our very best performance on the day. Like most marketing activities, conduct at an interview is largely a matter of common sense. But that common sense has to be applied in the preparation and management of our performance at the interview.

Reconnaissance

Find out what the client wants. What are the bees in his bonnet? What does he expect at the interview? What sort of organisation and approach is he looking for? What style of presentation does he prefer? There are several sources of information.

The most obvious source is the invitation itself. Read the invitation carefully, noting all direct information and instructions and looking carefully for any hidden messages in the text. Different clients write in different ways. Consider the state of mind and knowledge of the author and interpret the documents accordingly. If, for example, an American client refers to his program, the chances are that he means the architect's brief; his schedule (pronounced 'skedule') is the project time plan. If the documentation has been prepared by construction industry professionals or other experts, they will use the terms of their particular sector of the trade. Look out for the style of the lawyer, the civil servant or the contractually alert quantity surveyor. Each will write with precision but in an entirely different manner.

Speak directly to the client's representative and ask about the interview. What procedure will they adopt? Will there be a special time for us to make a presentation in our chosen form? Or will we be asked questions throughout? Is there an agenda? How will the room be arranged? What visual aids can they make available? How long will the interview last? Who are the panel, and what are their special interests? How many contenders are there? Who are they? Do not pursue questions that seem to embarrass or irritate the client, but do use this opportunity for contact to create or improve our friendly relationship with the client and make sure he knows that we are keen to give the job our best shot.

Choosing the interview team

Some people are good at interviews; others are not. The people we intend to put on the job may be better at providing a professional service than they are at presenting themselves at interviews. However, if we send our team of star presenters, they may impress the client, but when a completely different team turns up to do the job, the client will ask why. And we may develop a reputation for 'switch selling'—our industry's clientele inhabit a very small world!

The answer is a respectable compromise. Certain key people must be in the presentation team. In most projects, there is likely to be a technical element and a management element. A full-service architectural appointment will require a head designer and a project manager; a project management commission will require a project manager and a planning manager; a construction contract may require a construction manager and a commercial manager. These key people should be there. The projection of the firm's capability, however, can be made by other senior people who will not necessarily be directly involved in the performance of the work. And in the event, as we are in competition and we are presenting for more projects than we will ever secure, sometimes we will have committed some of the presenting team elsewhere before a decision is

121

taken.... However, in our balance of presenters and 'doers', we must always exclude anyone, however senior, who has become a proven liability at interviews.

Visual or audio-visual presentation

At a formal presentation, some form of visual or audiovisual aid is essential. The media available include video, overhead projector, 35 mm slides (possibly as part of a tape/slide presentation), flip charts and live computer graphics displays including demonstrations of CAD. The visual presentation must be professionally prepared and appropriately brief. We must not bore the pants off the client. It is neither possible nor desirable to tell our whole life history in a five minute visual presentation. We must limit what we have to say to the key messages. We may choose to concentrate on a brief visual slot or to illustrate our verbal presentation with text and photographic slides. Standard material must be carefully vetted for relevance and for any content, however trivial, that may alienate this particular client.

Rehearsal

However good we think we are and however many times we have done it before, we must get the presentation team together for a rehearsal. Even experienced teams find that something happens at the rehearsal that they would not have wished to happen in front of the client!

At the interview

The interview most likely to succeed takes the form of a friendly constructive discussion about the project, and leaves each party with a comfortable feeling about the prospect of working with the other. We should try to open the interview on a friendly informal basis with an exchange of pleasantries before the chairman embarks on the formal agenda. The ice, having been broken, is unlikely to reform. Our team leader must manage our performance throughout. He should watch the reactions of the interviewing panel and manage our team's input to respond to them. In particular, during technical sections of our programme, the leader must speed up the colleague who is going into more detail than the client wants to hear or slow down the other who has not sensed the client's deeper interest.

The client will ask key questions, the answers to which are very important to the success of the interview. 'Will these people you have brought here today do the job for us?' 'Do you always complete work on time?' 'The industry is busy, are you sure that you have sufficient resources to tackle the largest job you have ever had?' The first answer must always be positive. Any reservation or prudent qualification must follow. 'Yes, this is the team. But you will of course appreciate that if a decision is delayed, we are bidding for several jobs at the present time.' 'Yes, we have an enviable reputation for completing on time. You may have heard about... If we have the time one day, perhaps we could tell you the story of that. We learnt some valuable lessons.' 'Yes, we certainly have the resources. And we have already made a contingency arrangement to undertake elements of the work which may not have to be done locally, in our Manchester office.'

Two general points: we should not give the interviewers any reading material until the end of the presentation. They will read it instead of listening to us! After the interview, we should make sure that we debrief, for two reasons—to learn for the future, but more urgently to look for any difficulties we have created that might be capable of repair by some immediate further communication.

Negotiation

Some mention of negotiation is essential in this context. There are many good books on the topic, and it is only necessary here to reiterate some basic principles.

If our oft-repeated phrase, 'we must place ourselves in the position of the customer' is valid anywhere, it is valid in negotiation. In many cases, a little research, a great deal of thought and some calculation can give us enough information about the client's state of mind to make the negotiation seem like playing poker with our opponents' cards laid out on the table.

This is not necessarily to suggest that we want an outcome that places the client at a real disadvantage. Indeed our aim is for a happy, satisfied client. And we must remember that the kind of negotiations we are discussing here are likely to lead to the parties working together. The best negotiation, therefore, is the one after which both parties feel that they have done the best possible deal. We must not seek an unreasonable deal.

To put it in the simplest possible way: we must decide in advance what the ideal outcome would be for us and what is the worst we could live with. These are our 'target' and 'fall-back position'. If we can then estimate the same criteria for our opponent and note the reasons for them, it will usually be possible to identify some common ground acceptable to both parties. It is tempting to head straight for the common ground, but we must think of the psychology of winning or giving way. If either party 'wins' they must feel that they have worked for it. If either party has to give way, there should be as little loss of face as possible.

In most cases it is in neither party's interest for entrenched positions to be established at an early stage in the discussions. If our opponent digs in we will not find it easy to move him. If we commit ourselves to a position from which we can only retreat, we have placed a limit on what we can achieve. In general, if both parties are honestly seeking a mutually satisfactory conclusion, it is better to try to reach agreement on principles at first. As these are settled, discussions will move towards the point at which the price, or whatever else is under discussion, will be quite easy to determine.

11. The Marketing Audit

What is a marketing audit?

A full marketing audit takes stock of every aspect of our marketing activity and of other factors that affect it. Its aim is to make sure that we are in the right business, that we are offering the most appropriate products to the right customers at the optimum price and with the best possible sales messages—and that we are achieving the best possible results.

The Audit must ask four simple questions.

- What were our intentions?
- What are we actually doing?
- What are we achieving?
- What can we learn from the answers to the first three questions that will help us to decide what we should be doing to achieve more?

Such an audit may be undertaken at any time.

If audits are to be made regularly, some thought must be given to their frequency. We do not dig up the plants in the garden each week to see how they are growing. If we subject our marketing activity to potentially disturbing or even destructive scrutiny too often, we will deflect resources and attention away from marketing's essential purpose of providing the future lifeblood of the business.

We may think of running our marketing audit annually to match the financial audit, or perhaps every two years. However, it will be more appropriate in most organisations not to set a time interval but to conduct a formal audit when there are signs that it is necessary. These signs may include significant changes in external market conditions, new opportunities, internal reorganisation for non-market reasons, the emergence of a new competitor, an important product showing signs of reaching the point of decline. The audit can be held, in fact, at any time when we need to test the relevance and continued effectiveness of our efforts to obtain new work.

Any comprehensive review of our efforts may result in a significant change in our marketing and associated activities. It is therefore essential to register the status quo using a formal audit technique. We then have a firm base to work from, and the advantage of being able to repeat the same tests at a later date to measure what improvements have been made.

Who should undertake the audit? There is no definitive answer to that question, but there are some important qualifications for undertaking a marketing audit. These include technical marketing expertise, knowledge and understanding of the market sector, independence and availability.

If we have confidence in our own marketing management and staff, there is a strong case for them to do their own audit. If they are performing well and there is no reason to doubt their competence, they qualify for the job on all criteria other than that of independence. In the case of a self-audit, the leader of the team should set down the terms of reference for the audit, an outline methodology, a programme and a reporting format for agreement by the board, the managing director or the other appropriate supervising committee or individual to whom the final audit report will be submitted.

A measure of independence may be achieved by requiring individual units within a group business to carry out one another's marketing audits. Some sensitivity is required in managing this interaction between sibling rivals, but a certain amount of healthy 'needle' may well be exploited to ensure the thoroughness of the audit. And the next time, of course, auditor and audited may have changed places! Again, particularly if the participants are marketing practitioners rather than specialist marketing auditors, it is essential to map out the whole process before starting.

A group organisation which has a strong central internal audit department, whose terms of reference are not limited to the financial and accounting functions, may be tempted to add marketing to its audit capability. This may be appropriate in certain circumstances—such as during a period of rapid change or a spate of acquisitions—but in general, if the necessary level of expertise is available, it would almost certainly be better employed in marketing *per se*.

Alternatively, an external consultant can be employed. If we need an independent expert view, bringing some new and creative ideas into play, this should be the most appropriate course. Everything depends, however, on selecting the right consultant and getting the terms of reference right —find the right person and ask the right question! This is more easily said than done. Look again at the four criteria: technical marketing expertise, knowledge and understanding of the market sector, independence and availability. They apply as much to an external as to an internal auditor.

The manager who defines a management consultant as 'someone who is paid to borrow your watch to tell you the time' is commenting on his own ability to select and manage external help. Indeed, if you cannot tell the time, have the misfortune to be too short-sighted to see the watch on the end of your arm, or even just need to be quite sure that your colleagues believe you when you tell them the time, there is a case for paying an expert to look at your watch for you. In other words, a properly-used consultant will bring expertise which is not available in-house, will see things clearly which for any reason you cannot see for yourself, and should have the credibility of an acknowledged expert.

Using an external marketing auditor, however, should not be the first option. If we have a cold in the head or a touch of flu we take an aspirin and push on. If we have symptoms that suggest something more seriously wrong with us, we go to see the doctor. A decision on bringing in external advice must depend on the level of expertise available in-house and the scale and nature of the issues to be tackled. Corporate cultures vary in their enthusiasm for the use of external consultants: this too will be a factor.

As noted above, the first requirement of our marketing auditor is that he should have the necessary technical marketing expertise coupled with the knowledge and understanding necessary to be able to apply that expertise to our market sector. As we have seen, the broad principles of marketing are common to all commercial and professional endeavour, but its practice varies between business sectors. The major body of marketing expertise has been developed in the fast-moving consumer goods sector. The business-to-business marketing of services, into which most construction industry activities fall, is a specialist area. Construction itself is an even narrower area of expertise. In selecting our consultant, we must make sure that his experience and vision is broad enough to enable him to take a global view, while his knowledge of our sector is such that we will not be paying him to discover our industry, but only to understand the particular needs of our organisation at the present time. This is the second requirement.

The third criterion is independence. We need objective analysis, and advice that is not affected by any commercial interest other than our own. Most consultants—especially marketing consultants, if they are any good at marketing—want to sell us a follow-up service. The best will not let it show, and will rely on our recognising the objectivity of their advice to bring us back another time for more. The modern business world is a complex place, and most of us cannot avoid cross-relationships in business matters. The important thing is to make sure that if there are unavoidable conflicts of interest, they are in the open where they can be provided for. Our marketing intentions are probably the most commercially sensitive information in the organisation. Considerable care in keeping them to ourselves is justified.

The final requirement is availability. Will we get the person who sold us the job, or will the sorcerer disappear after a few days and leave us to the tender mercies of his apprentice? We considered this from the other side of the deal in chapter 10. It is very tempting to send in the sales team and later switch to the 'doing' team. On the basis that 'it takes one to spot one', we should be alive to this possibility and make sure that we know what we are buying.

When appointing an external consultant to undertake a marketing audit, it is essential that all the parameters of the appointment are agreed in writing before a commitment is made. Clearly agreed terms of reference come first. What is the aim of the audit, who is the 'client' for the auditor's contract, what access does the auditor have to other people for information gathering, what type of report is required, in what form and addressed to whom? And so on. Programme dates must be clear. The fee, and precisely what service it covers or does not cover, must be clearly defined. If it is not a lump sum, there should be a firmly agreed and realistic budget.

In tying down an effectively binding contract, remember that we are employing an expert for his expertise. It is our business we are dealing with, and our money which is paying for it—but do let us be careful not to so restrict the marketing auditor by the terms of the contract that it becomes our own audit rather than that of the consultant we are paying to do it.

And so to the meat of the marketing audit. The following discussion of a marketing audit is not offered as a rigid format, and is by no means the only possibility. However, it follows a logical sentence with the intention that it may be adapted and developed to suit individual needs and circumstances.

What were our intentions?

The very first step in the audit is to record, as fully and as accurately as possible, our stated intentions for marketing. It is important here that we do not cheat, because one of the first aims of the marketing audit is to test the quality of our business policy making, our marketing strategy, our plans for action and our budgeted resources.

In this first stage of the audit, we therefore assemble all existing documentation as to the type and volume of business we hoped to do, the products and services we intended to offer, the customers to whom we were to offer them, who was to do the offering and how, and so on. We need to know what our intentions were and, if possible, the reasoning behind them. If we have prepared a formal marketing strategy, most of this information will be quite easy to find. If we have not, we must look for any relevant policy papers, minutes of meetings at which marketing intentions were discussed, internal memoranda suggesting that a particular sort of business should be pursued. If we are looking for business, even if we have not prepared a formal marketing strategy, there will be some statement about what we are trying to do.

We may include the following documents, among others, in this dossier of our intentions.

- Company articles of association
- Business plans or strategies
- Marketing strategy
- Marketing and sales budgets
- Board minutes
- Reports from management consultants
- Reports from non-executive directors
- Policy statements
- Management charts
- Policy instructions to marketing/sales staff
- Terms of reference for individuals

In collecting this documentation we must bear in mind that it will be used for two purposes. The first is to compare what we are actually doing with what we had decided to do; the second is to review the intentions themselves.

What are we actually doing?

We must now schedule all our actual efforts to get new work. Who is doing it? What tactics are they adopting? How are they doing it? How are they recording, managing, communicating and reporting? What systems are in place? What are we spending, on what, and how is cost being monitored and controlled? This is a schedule of activity, of resources, of systems and of methods. We are not concerned here with achievement, planned or real, but with effort and the mechanics of activities directed towards getting new work.

The following list may be useful in suggesting the kind of activities that could be described in this section of the information gathering phase.

- Market research
- Customer information gathering
- Direct mail
- Personal approach by letter or telephone
- Advertising
- Exhibitions
- Sponsorship
- Corporate hospitality
- Below the line publicity

There are many more. Because an activity is included in this list it is not necessarily something that we should be doing. Advertising is an example. In certain circumstances it may be an indispensable element of our marketing; in others it may be a waste of money. Whatever we are doing in the name of 'marketing'—and people do find some abstruse things to charge to their marketing budgets—we must record it.

What are we achieving?

Our marketing activity has a number of intermediate objectives. In sequence, these may include:

- acquiring information about potential clients
- establishing business-generating relationships
- obtaining enquiries
- securing contracts.

The third element of our marketing audit is to record what we are achieving at each of these separate levels.

These headings are likely to be generally applicable. But some thought must be given to the nature of the marketing process within our own business to make sure that we record our achievements in the way that best serves the purposes of the audit.

Information

A small organisation may be able to schedule all the potential customers in which it has a named individual to approach. A larger one may find it better to rely on summary statistical data. In either case, we must first define what is an organisation within a target sector, and what is useful information about it. Assessing the quality and quantity of the information we have gathered is at best a very inexact science. We must take great care that the exercise does not run away with us and become an end in itself. Here is a classic opportunity for the statistical or analytical buff, who may also be addicted to PC databases, to create an exercise in which the precision of the data handling process far exceeds the quality of the input. When we come at the next stage to analyse this information, our aim will be to determine whether we are getting the best information to support our initial approaches to potential customers. This 'information about information' should provide no more than a practical, approximate guide to that end.

Relationships

Asking ourselves what we have achieved in terms of enquiry-generating relationships is the most tricky of these data-collecting activities. We are primarily concerned with registered relationships with individual in potential customer organisations, which have been gained as a result of systematic efforts to create them in chosen target sectors. If we have a system for recording these, there should be no problem. If we have not, discovering this will be an important outcome of the audit. We need to define 'relationship' for our own business. In general it will be a situation in which the parties have had direct contact by exchange of correspondence, telephone or a face-to-face meeting, the individual is recognised to be in a deciding or other position which may affect us, in an organisation which may have business to give us, and both parties expect further contact in the reasonably near future.

Enquiries

There should be no difficulty in bringing together a schedule of current enquiries. We must decide whether, for the purposes of the audit, we are considering the enquiries that are live at a point in time defined for the audit, or whether we are looking at the flow of enquiries into the business during a recent historical period, say the latest accounting year. This is a matter for us to decide in the light of our own business. In most cases, as we are looking forward to the profitable work we intend to obtain, the point-in-time approach is likely to prove more appropriate.

Some thought must be given to the presentation of the enquiry data. It is first of all necessary to sort enquiries by the stage that has been reached in getting them on board and processing them. One of the most effective categorisations for this purpose is that suggested in chapter 4:

- potential enquiries
- active enquiries
- potential contracts.

Definitions of these stages which suit our own business are as important here as they are for the management and reporting of the enquiry-handling process itself. The same definitions should be used.

In all but the simplest of cases, we must categorise our enquiries not only by the stage they have reached in our handling process, but by other factors to do with the enquiry itself. Value is, of course, the first factor. The range of values we handle will depend on our business. Within the range, there will be thresholds that affect the way we view or handle the project. Projects below a certain value may go into the small works department. At the other end of the scale, there may be a size of project for which we set up a special multi-discipline team. Other factors will include the geographical location of the site, the nature of the work, the time at which it is likely to be carried out, the commercial conditions that affect likely risk and margin, and so on. One special piece of information which should be attached to each enquiry is how and why we received it; this will be important in our evaluation of the effectiveness of our various efforts to gain work. If, for example, we have ten salesmen yet all our new business is generated by contacts made by the chairman, we should know about it. Perhaps more significantly, we should know when the chairman only thinks that they are made by him.

Division of the current enquiry schedule into various categories will provide the most meaningful information at the next stage when we come to analyse the data we have collected. Again, we must avoid any waste of time and resources or, worse still, distortion of the results of the audit, by over-detailed management of our data.

Orders received

This should be the most straightforward information to collect. We need a schedule of new contracts by client type, product, geographical location, date of order, accounting period for execution and payment etc. Once again we must choose our own data and aim to strike the balance that provides the most useful information with the least effort and disruption.

What can we learn and what should we be doing to achieve more?

Now that we have a clear statement of what we intended to do, what we did and what we have achieved by doing it, we must ask a number of searching questions. Are we achieving our business objectives for the marketing function? If so, is it because of the marketing strategy or in spite of it? Do we have a clear and effective marketing strategy which segments our market and tells us precisely what we should be doing in each segment? Is there evidence that our segmentation and our allocation of priorities between segments reflect what we now know about the market?

In the light of the answers to these questions, and others which will inevitably arise from the mass of data we have gathered, we are now in a position to repeat, if we so wish, the process of marketing strategy preparation along the lines described in chapters 2 and 3.

And are we missing anything?

This is the final question in the analysis. We have a systematic, and perhaps therefore somewhat pedestrian, approach to getting business. But do we have antennae to identify unplanned opportunities? Do we ever dismiss an opportunity just because it is not within a target sector, a sector chosen perhaps for ease of marketing rather than production? When we recognise such an opportunity, are we flexible enough to be able to respond to it? Are we indeed flexible enough, without being so flabby that we abandon our marketing strategy at the drop of a hat, to recognise changes in the market-place, changes in competition, changes in our own capacity and new technological opportunities; and to adjust our strategy to enable us to respond to them?

Suggested further reading

Connor, Dick and Davidson, Jeffrey P. *Marketing your consulting and professional services*. John Wiley & Sons, London, 1990.
A very American text to English eyes, but full of practical techniques for obtaining 'service' business.

Davidson, Hugh. *Offensive marketing*. Penguin Business, London, 1987.
A rather more advanced book, subtitled '*or how to make your competitors followers*', which will capture the imagination.

Hingston, Peter. *The (greatest) sales and marketing book*. Hingston, 1989.
The practical action guide for a small business. Not specifically directed at the 'service' sector into which most construction marketing falls, but because it is aimed at small businesses it offers a great deal of simply stated common sense.

Ivanovic, A. (ed. P. H. Collin). *Dictionary of marketing*. Peter Collin Publishing.
A paperback dictionary giving definitions of most marketing, sales and associated commercial terms, 1989.

Naisbitt, John and Aburdene, Patricia. *Megatrends 2000*. Pan, 1990.
An updated version of John Naisbitt's original 1982 'Megatrends'; a powerful reminder of the worldwide forces that continue to govern our economic and personal lives.

Olins, Wally. *Corporate identity*. Thames and Hudson, London, 1989.
Making business strategy visible through design: the definitive work on corporate identity. A book which is not only valuable reading, but a pleasure to have.

Pennant-Rea, Rupert and Emmott, Bill. *The pocket economist*. 1985. Nobes, Christopher. *The pocket accountant*. Hindle, Tim. *The pocket banker*. Basil Blackwell, 1983 and *The Economist*, 1985.
Not strictly marketing books, but a trilogy of popular basic texts which provide an insight into worlds closely adjacent to that of marketing.

Peters, Thomas J. and Waterman, Robert H. Jr. *In search of excellence*. Harper & Row, London, 1982.
Eight basic characteristics of the USA's most successful companies.

Richardson, B. G. *The CIRIA construction information guide*. CIRIA and E. & F. N. Spon, London, 1989.
A comprehensive guide to sources of information for the construction industry.

Wilmshurst, John. *The fundamentals and practice of marketing.* Heinemann Professional Publishing on behalf of the Chartered Institute of Marketing, 1984.

John Wilmshurst's very readable book is specifically designed to cover the syllabus requirements of the Chartered Institute of Marketing.

Index

137